FIRST, AND BEFORE ALL THINGS

FIRST, AND BEFORE ALL THINGS

Kate Wilby

The Book Guild Ltd

First published in Great Britain in 2019 by
The Book Guild Ltd
9 Priory Business Park
Wistow Road, Kibworth
Leicestershire, LE8 0RX
Freephone: 0800 999 2982
www.bookguild.co.uk
Email: info@bookguild.co.uk
Twitter: @bookguild

Typeset in Adobe Garamond Pro

Printed and bound by CPI Group (UK) Ltd, Croydon, CR0 4YY

ISBN 978 1912881 291

British Library Cataloguing in Publication Data.
A catalogue record for this book is available from the British Library.

'For those I love, and those I have lost'

‘First, and before all things’

That this woman hath done will be told for a memorial of her

CONTENTS

AUTHOR'S NOTE

LUNATICKS

In her will, Mary used the term 'lunaticks' (later spelt 'lunatics') to describe people experiencing a disorder of the mind. It was a commonly accepted word in the seventeenth century and its use in this story is not intended to cause offence. Other terms used at the time have also been included. Please look at reputable organisations for a discussion of the currently acceptable ways to describe people experiencing mental ill health.

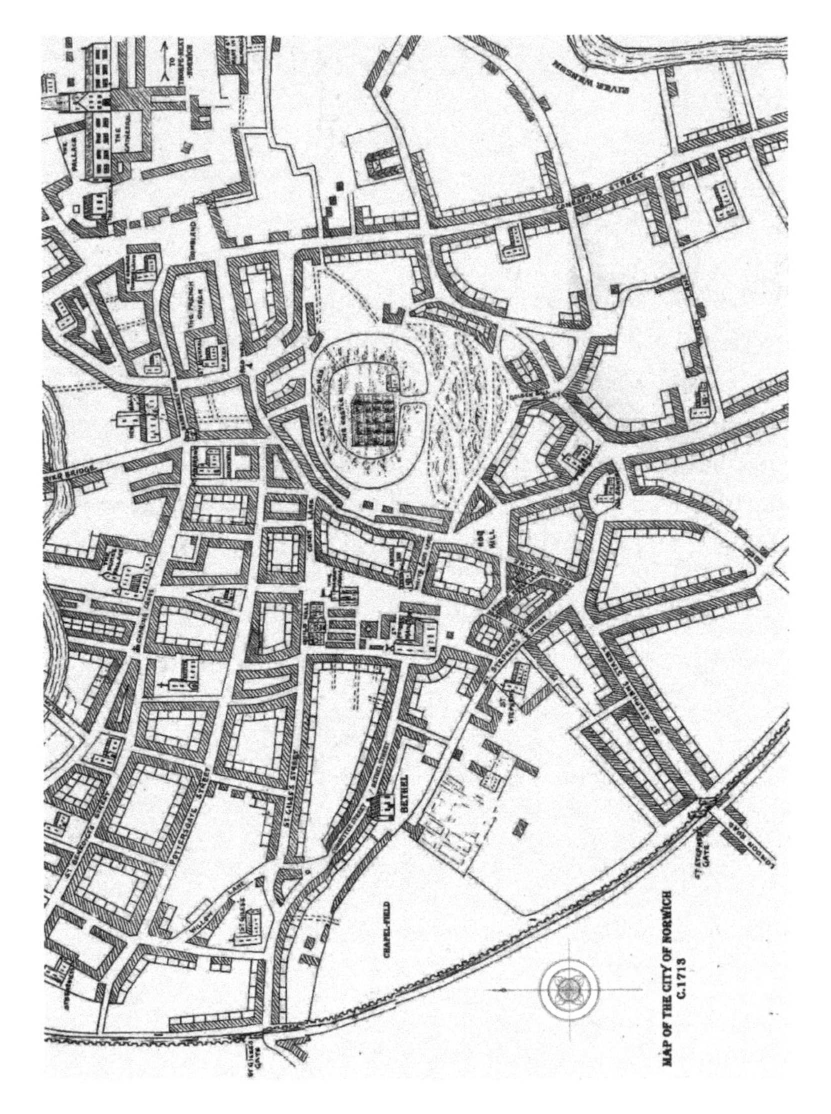

Map of the city of Norwich,
from Cleer's Map, 1696

TIMELINE

Historical Events *Events in Mary's life*

JAMES I (R. 1603–1625) HOUSE OF STUART

1603 Accession of James I of England, King James VI of Scotland
1605 Catholic plot to blow up the Houses of Parliament (5th November)
1606* *John Mann (Mary's father) born*
1608 Norwich Public Library established, the first library in England
1616* *Hester Bacon (Mary's mother) born*
1625 Plague in Norwich
1625 King James I of England died

CHARLES I (R. 1625–1649)

1625 Accession of Charles I of England; he believed kings to be 'little Gods on Earth'
1627 *John Mann admitted to the Freedom of Norwich*
1630 Plague in Norwich
1631 *Samuel Chapman born*
1638 *John Mann married Hester Bacon*
1642 First English Civil War. Charles I raised his standard at Nottingham on 22nd August

1644 Oliver Cromwell became Lieutenant General of the Eastern Association Army

1645 Parliament established the New Model Army; Sir Thomas Fairfax was Lord General, and Oliver Cromwell was Lieutenant General, his second-in-command

1647 *Mary Ann Mann born (24th March)*

1648 *The Great Blowe, Norwich (24th April)*

1648 Second English Civil War (17th–19th August)

1649 Charles I tried for treason and beheaded

THE INTERREGNUM (1649–1660)

1649 *John Mann became Sheriff of Norfolk*

1650 *John Mann became Captain of the Militia in Norwich*

1653 *John Mann became Mayor of Norwich*

1653 Oliver Cromwell installed as Lord Protector

1656 *Samuel Chapman awarded MA, Corpus Christi College, Cambridge*

1658 Death of Oliver Cromwell

1658 Richard Cromwell succeeded his father as Lord Protector

1659 Richard Cromwell stood down

CHARLES II (R. 1660–1685) RESTORATION OF THE MONARCHY

1660 Restoration of Charles II

1661 Coronation of Charles II, King of England

1661 Oliver Cromwell's remains were exhumed and posthumously 'executed'

1664 *John Mann benefited Norwich Public Library*

1665 War was proclaimed against France

1665 Plague in London

1665 Plague in Norwich
1666 Great Fire of London
1667 *Hester Mann, Mary's mother, died (Mary aged 20)*
1669 *John Mann married Dorothy Fountayn*
1669 Smallpox outbreak in Norwich
1670 *Samuel Chapman became rector of Thorpe Episcopi in Thorpe-next-Norwich*
1671 Charles II visited Norwich
1676 Bedlam moved to new buildings in Moorfields, London
1677 Doughty's Hospital established in Norwich
1682 *Mary Mann married Samuel Chapman on 10th May (Mary aged 35, Samuel 51)*
1682 Sir Thomas Browne died, notable physician and philosopher
1685 Charles II died

KING JAMES II (R. 1685–1688)

1685 Accession of King James II, King of England (second son of Charles I)
1685 Monmouth Rebellion, an unsuccessful rebellion led by Charles II's eldest illegitimate son, James Scott the 1st Duke of Monmouth, who attempted to overthrow the unpopular King James II (his uncle)
1685 The Royal Norfolk Regiment was raised during the Monmouth Rebellion
1688 The Glorious Revolution, also called the 'Bloodless Revolution', led to the overthrow of King James II of England (James VII of Scotland) by a union of English parliamentarians and William, Prince of Orange

KING WILLIAM III (WILLIAM OF ORANGE) (R. 1688–1702) AND QUEEN MARY II (R. 1688–1694)

1688 Accession of King William III and Queen Mary II (executive authority rested with William)
1692 Glencoe Massacre
1694 Queen Mary died; William of Orange continued to reign
1695 *John Mann died (Mary aged 48)*
1697 New coin minted
1700 *Samuel Chapman died, aged 69 (Mary aged 53)*
1701 *Norwich Post* newspaper began publication, the first outside London
1702 William of Orange died

QUEEN ANNE (R. 1702–1714)

1702 Accession of Queen Anne of England, Scotland and Ireland
1707 Act of Union
1712 *Trustees on behalf of Mary Chapman leased land*
1712 *Building agreement for the Bethel Hospital signed*
1713 *The Bethel Hospital completed*
1714 Queen Anne died

KING GEORGE I (R. 1714–1727) HOUSE OF HANOVER

1714 King George I (change of dynasty to the House of Hanover)
1720 Riot in Norwich
1724 *Mary Chapman died, 8th January, aged 76*

* approximate date

One

'FIRST, AND BEFORE ALL THINGS'

MARY, 1724

First, and before all things, I ask you to take a look at the grim portrait of me that hangs in the boardroom of the hospital I founded. What do you see? An old woman in her widow's black? I admit, there is a likeness, but, truly, I hardly recognise myself, for I look stern, sour and unforgiving, certainly not full of passion and joy. Perhaps, in my later years, this dark, dour creature is how I appeared to others. Yet I am disappointed that the artist has not captured the essence of me. There is none of that spark I have felt since I can remember, nor any hint of the joy I have experienced in my life. And where is the evidence of that great love that I shared? Why is it not showing in my face, shining out for all to see? And so, I wonder. Did I really change from being a lively, loved, young girl, and then a joyous, passionate woman, into this dark, decrepit, lonely being? The portrait does not tell the whole story of my life and it does not capture all that I am, and all that I have been. As I near the end of my time on earth, I look back over the years and I am content. I have left a legacy, a place of hope and a testament to love, and I pray that it will endure long after I have been called to God. I have tried to do good, for all of my life, and I can only hope that it will be enough, for I will leave it to Him to make the final judgement.

I was born in 1647, the third daughter of the richest and most powerful man in Norwich, at a time when our city was a thriving centre of culture and trade, second only to London. I was born into brutal, turbulent times, in the midst of the English Civil Wars. I was witness to the fight between king and Parliament, the fight for rights and liberties, at a time when men could behead a king and a king had the power to execute a dead man. I saw seven monarchs and two Lord Protectors in my lifetime, then a bloodless revolution, and the rise of the ordinary man. I saw whole families wiped out by the plague, and others decimated and scarred by smallpox, though most of my loved ones, by the grace of God, survived. But we were not unscathed.

I also witnessed many wonders. I saw stars explode across the sky, boats being rowed along our flooded streets, and skaters, even a market, on a frozen river. I was shaken by a devastating explosion that carpeted our streets with glass, and blood, though our fine city recovered and rebuilt. I lived amongst a great mix of people. The good, the mad and the sad. Soldiers, Strangers, story-tellers, and souls from other shores. I saw the rich, and the rich of spirit, and how each lived their lives. Rebels, thieves, witches. Lunaticks. Mad men. Hangings in ditches. All this I saw, all a source of wonder.

At home I witnessed the pain of those close to me, as they suffered from the most agonising mental distress. And I saw the torments of their kin, who watched and worried, but were truly unable to help, or to offer the mad any respite from the terrors that inhabited their poor distracted minds.

As a gentlewoman I was fortunate to live with wealth, comfort and privilege. But, of course, as a woman of those times, when men truly ruled the world, I had limited power over my own destiny. Indeed, with little thought for my wants, let alone my happiness, and unaware of my hidden desires, my father appointed me as carer to those in my family who had lost their reason. Yet I understood his decision, for there was simply no one else, and what could I do but accept this as my duty, albeit perhaps a little grudgingly on occasion? I chose to do good, for the whole of my life, and I faithfully carried out that duty. Though my life, my glorious life, was not as dreary as it may sound.

With first-hand experience of insanity in my family and others close to me, I grew comfortable in the presence of lunaticks, and was neither fearful nor disgusted. And neither did I judge. So, I was horrified to hear the stories that reached us from London, of the cruel treatment of the lunaticks at that monstrous asylum, the Bedlam – disturbing images that I could not forget, and which would impel me for the rest of my days. I knew that to torment those poor wretches, those damaged souls, was wrong. But how could I have foreseen that, out of compassion for those whom I saw all around me in such a woeful state, I would establish the first hospital outside London built solely for the treatment of lunaticks. A place of kindness and safety, where there was hope that those deprived of their senses would be cured, to return home, to live out their lives – to be at peace. And I certainly would not have thought that there would be men, in our benevolent city, who would try to prevent me from creating such a place. Men whose actions might be considered understandable in all the fear and confusion of those times, but whose true motives were cleverly concealed.

Perhaps I should have seen that I would inherit the strength and determination of my father, and the kindness and charity of my mother, qualities that would serve me well in the fight to come. But I had been living a lonely life, a carer of the tormented: a life devoid of power, devoid of passion. How could I have known that I would not only experience the most profound love, with the most wonderful of men, but that I would build a sanctuary as a lasting testament to that love?

I have steadfastly resolved to keep myself in the love of God, to whom I owe my being and my well-being. I have lived at the

Bethel Hospital in Norwich since it was built in 1713, perhaps as a way to feel closer to my beloved, my Samuel, and to others I have lost. But also, to ensure it was run as we had envisioned. And, certainly, to do good.

I will tell you my story and I hope that, after hearing it, you will take another look at my portrait and see perhaps the hint of amusement in my eyes and a reflection of the life I have lived. I hope you will see me, really see me, as I truly was.

Two

'MY FATHER, JOHN MANN, MAYOR OF NORWICH'

I ask you to bear with me, for it is important that I begin my story with my father, he who made me, for he was there at the very beginning, at that great explosion that shook our city, and his faith saw me through to the very end.

My father was my hero. He was respected by his fellow aldermen, business associates, friends and servants. And he was adored by his family. He loved to talk, to tell tales. He lived every part of his life, fully and without regret. To my mother he was her protector, her one and only. And to his young second wife he was her lusty man. Those who knew him would describe his strength, his vigour and his determination. His friends also talked of his loyalty and his generosity, though all, without hesitation, would use just one word to sum him up – powerful.

I would describe him another way – as my abiding inspiration – for, over the years, I have lost count of the times I have had cause to thank his belief in me.

My father was born to Samuel Mann, a merchant, who rose to prominence and married well, to Anne Ferrier, a daughter of the mayor. My father often said it was not surprising that, as one of twelve children, no one remembered his birth date with any certainty. But I disagree: someone should have remembered, his parents most of all. My own father and mother had eleven children and made sure to mark each one of our birth dates in some way.

It is not so difficult. Though not unkind or cruel, his parents were simply too preoccupied with themselves and the trappings of high office to take much notice of their children, let alone show any of them much love. For my father, that was the story of his early years, and he had a tough and lonely time. My father seldom talked of his parents, but through small details that he sometimes let slip we gained a little understanding of his bleak childhood. Now I can see that perhaps it was his experiences in his early life that forged his determination to be successful. He once said that even as a young boy he knew he would simply work and work until he had enough money to provide a comfortable life for his family, so that those he loved would never be in need. But I think it was more than that – it was as if the loneliness of his childhood created in him a desire to be a better father than his own had been, determined to make time for his children, and to show them more gentleness and love than had been shown to him.

His own father, though lacking the ability to show any affection, was at least able to use his status and influence to secure a trade for his sons and good marriages for his daughters. Thus, my father gained a position as a tailor's apprentice, to Edward Thompson, a respected member of one of the leading Norwich guilds. My father, true to his word, worked hard, and in 1627 he was admitted to the Freedom of Norwich. Now a member of the Worsted Weavers Company, he was permitted to trade in the city. Over the next few years he became established as a master tailor and built up his workshop, taking on his own apprentices and journeymen. As a freeman he was able to choose a wife, but he chose not to, preferring instead to work, and, spending little on himself, he saw his wealth grow. When he felt he was able to provide for a family he began to consider getting wed, though a few more years would pass until he met somebody he deemed suitable, my mother, Hester Bacon. In 1638, after a long courtship, which my father bore with fortitude and my mother with some amusement, she finally accepted him, and they were married. Without delay they set about creating their family, with a son John, followed soon after by a daughter, Hester. My father was clearly keen on his role in the begetting of children, and another son and daughter would arrive before I made my own very determined appearance. My father loved to tell the tale of how my mother had been taking a stroll around the garden, trying to ease her discomfort, for I had been wriggling around inside her for weeks, when, suddenly overcome with pain, she gave one great push and I slipped out with a splat amongst the camomile, keen to be getting on with life.

My father was the traditional head of the household, with a strong sense of duty and obligation to his family. He was devout, always sure to be seen conducting himself according to the precepts set out in the good book, and he quickly gained respect within our community and, later, with his fellow city aldermen. And those contacts, in turn, helped him to build up his business. My mother, though feisty and outspoken, accepted her role as the wife of a successful merchant. She had children to raise and servants to organise. She knew how important it was to my father for his family to reflect his growing status, and she ensured we were always well dressed and well mannered. Though privately she despaired of entertaining some of the more frivolous and less learned wives of my father's friends, she always played her part when called upon, and was well known for her excellent suppers.

My mother was younger than my father, by ten years or so, and I know she rebelled at times over his dominance and made sure he did not win every argument. But she also accepted that he gave her a good life, certainly a better life than many other women of our time. We knew how fortunate we were – we only had to look around our city to know. We were settled and comfortable, and over the years, as my father became even more successful, our wealth and standing in the community increased further.

But there were turbulent times ahead, brutal times of divided loyalties and civil war. The country lived through the execution of a king for treason and the formation of a Republic, then, in time, the restoration of a new king to the throne.

And my father? Well, the mighty John Mann, future mayor of Norwich and the wealthiest man in our city, not only survived these times – he flourished.

MY FATHER'S RISE TO POWER

In 1625, when my father was still an apprentice and the people of Norwich were recovering from an outbreak of plague, the popular King James I died and his son was installed as King Charles I. Charles believed in the ultimate power of the Crown and enjoyed asserting himself, though many felt he did not convince as a king. He needed to raise money after his unsuccessful wars against France and Spain and demanded so-called 'loans' or 'free gifts' from local wealthy men, many of whom resisted and who were imprisoned for their lack of loyalty. Yet, despite this threat to their freedom, the people of Norwich, as elsewhere, continued to rebel against the king's demands.

Many ordinary people had had enough of seeing their hard-earned money being taken by the king for his pointless wars, and they were further angered by the rumours that the money he raised was being spent on his personal art collection. Some complained in private or when in the company of their close friends, though few took any action. But when the king demanded 'two ships of war' from each major town, the mayor of Norwich made a stand and refused to provide them. This small rebellion irritated the king and in response he issued two writs of *quo warranto* against the mayor, challenging his right to hold office. The mayor stood his ground and stood trial, and his courage was rewarded. He was well advised and had only to prove that, in refusing the king's request, he had solely employed the power that he had been authorised to use as elected mayor, and, therefore, he had not abused his power at all – the rather ingenious use of this argument meant that there was no alternative but for the charges against him to be discharged.

As a young man, my father had watched the mayor's stand against the king with interest, noting that courage and strength seemed to come more easily to some men, and to powerful men in particular. This act of defiance by the mayor of Norwich was a sign that, despite the king's belief in his divine right, the Crown did not hold all the power. Above all, it was a victory for the ordinary man. And perhaps it was the memory of this courageous stand against authority that persuaded many in Norwich, including my father, to side with Parliament and against the king, in the Civil Wars to come.

It was rumoured that the king was also planning to restore the Catholic faith, and, like many people in England in those times, my father followed the one true religion. He had been born into a strongly Protestant family and believed that we should be ruled by a Protestant king. My father had grown up through the 1630s, when Puritan values had flourished and as he listened to the words being spoken by the great Puritan preachers, those godly men, my father understood that all areas of life should be lived according to Christian principles – a belief which he maintained throughout his life.

His family grew, year upon year (my poor mother), and we were raised to accept that all our life belonged to God and that, whether at work, in the home or in church, we should dedicate ourselves wholly to serving Him. Fortunately for us, my father was not one of those strict Puritans who took pleasure in removing all joy from life. We were a devout family, but my father still enjoyed spending his money. Times were changing, and it was no longer only the great and the rich who could afford to live well. My father and his fellow businessmen were spending their hard-earned fortunes, ensuring that others could see how richly they lived. He also loved to see the delight created by the luxuries and small gifts that he brought home from his trips to London. I could, as I look back, perhaps have shown a little more pleasure myself, for I was a very pious little girl and looked upon his trinkets with some disdain. My poor, generous father. He took my rejection quietly and hid his disappointment and would try again on his next visit. When I learnt to read, and he realised that I treasured books, he would always return with some small volume for me, pleased and relieved to meet with my approval. I can see now, with a love that warms me, that he knew me well, even then.

Fortunately for my father, at that time one of the godly men himself, all honourable occupation was seen as a means of glorifying God, so, whilst he worked to build his business, he was also serving God. And, as diligence in one's calling was a virtue, he could work hard, and make money, and yet still serve God. My father was a happy man. Devout. And rich.

My father liked to tell of the times leading up to the Civil Wars, believing we should learn that part of our history well, for it influenced all that came after. He would only explain one side of the conflict though, his side, the side of right, the side of the common man, the godly man. I could see that the supporters of the king were also committed to their beliefs, and that perhaps my father did not tell us the whole story. Of course, I questioned him on his principles, though in those days I knew that, for all his kindliness, it was pointless to argue with him over matters of politics and business. Still, I thought over his words and quietly came to my own conclusions, for I, too, felt strongly about the rights of the common man and was proud to be from a family of loyal parliamentarians. We mixed with people with the same ideals, and that would be to my advantage in my later years, as I fought to pursue God's purpose for me.

ROUNDHEADS AND ROYALISTS

I was still just one of the many twinkles in my father's eye when the bloody battles of the Civil War were fought. On one side were the supporters of King Charles I, the royalists, who accepted the king's ultimate supremacy over Church and state. Against the royalists were those who fought for the rights of parliamentary rule, believing that the king's powers should be limited and that religion was a matter of individual conscience. To the royalists, the parliamentarians were 'Roundheads', named after the shaved heads of the London apprentices who had so strongly supported Parliament in the months before the true fighting began. Royalists versus Roundheads, the two factions, each strong in their beliefs and each willing to accept the deaths of thousands of men for their cause.

There were many royalists in Norwich, but over the years recruitment to the parliamentary forces spread, initially amongst the apprentices, and then helped by the increasing number of Puritans in the city. The newly powerful Oliver Cromwell, a Puritan and the MP for Cambridge, who opposed the rule of Charles I, was showing his ability as a military commander, first with the Eastern Association Army and then as second-in-command of the New Model Army. Cromwell's loyal, well-organised and well-supported forces would fight many battles and go on to defeat the king, beginning years of uncertainty and resulting, eventually, in the bloody and bitter fall of the monarchy.

The most powerful men in Norwich, the city aldermen, and by then that included my father, sided with Parliament, but the people of Norwich were divided – some were for the king and some against. Despite this, my father always said that there was never any real fighting in Norwich because people were tolerant folk and would live close to those of the opposing political persuasion, even whilst disagreeing with them. Besides, Norwich was thriving, and people were too busy building up their trades for any serious disagreements to surface, and they would swiftly put aside their differences when there were deals to be done.

During the years of the Civil Wars my father continued to work, expand his business and build a family, but he learnt to tread carefully and to speak cautiously. He said that those years helped him to develop his political astuteness, as well as his expertise in debate and negotiation. Already quite wily, these were skills that he would use to his advantage throughout his political life, and also, at times, often with my mother, and occasionally with me, to ease his way in his personal life.

My father would often be accompanied by a little trail of people as he walked about the city, fellow weavers and merchants, who followed closely behind him, as if in hope that they might also benefit from his good fortune. He would rub his whiskered face as he dispensed business advice to any who cared to listen, though he was quick to discourage those who were foolish enough to think he might invest any of his hard-earned money in their schemes. At home he was quieter, and I remember that his hands were always full, heavy with coins, overflowing with the rich cloth he sold, or holding a book and a mug of his favourite ale.

He associated mainly with those who shared his beliefs, amongst whom he could talk freely, at the Angel Inn, the largest coaching inn in Norwich. The Angel served food of a reasonable quality, and copious amounts of ale, beer and brandy. As well as providing lodgings, the Angel also housed auction rooms and gambling halls for travellers and merchants going about their business. Situated between the Cattle Market and the Castle Ditches, not far from the church of St Peter Mancroft and my childhood home, the Angel was always a hive of activity, where my father would go to observe the world and to do deals with the cloth traders. He once told of visiting another inn, where he was horrified to hear the king's health being drunk to loud cheers, and wisely my father had slipped away when the locals started singing bawdy songs about Cromwell. He learnt which inns to avoid, and he knew that the soldiers of the parliamentary army in Norwich had the sense to avoid them too. Why cause trouble when there was no need? For you could be working alongside a royalist the next day when you were both sober and no longer looking for an argument.

In May 1646, Charles I surrendered to the Scottish army. In the aftermath, as England experienced further eruptions of violence, my father had his own eruption, resulting in my birth the following March. These were uncertain times for the country, but it seems nothing could stop my father from adding to his much-desired family. I was my parents' third daughter, their fifth child, and we had all survived, so far at least. Life was not looking so good for the king, who was still a prisoner of the Scots, for he was then handed over to his enemy, the parliamentarians, for money.

Despite divided loyalties amongst the people of Norwich there was just one major disturbance in the uneasy peace between the royalists and parliamentarians. In April 1648, a rebellion led by a crowd of royalists prompted a riot that only ended after a great explosion at the site of the city's armoury, which blew out the windows of the nearby churches, and was so loud it was heard all across the county. They say it was like the sky was raining destruction, the day of the Great Blowe, with glass, timber and stone falling all around, creating a deathly haze that spread across the city. As a baby, I had been woken, screaming with annoyance, by the detonation of the gunpowder spilled during the riot. I would not be calmed, and my mother had to hold me, safe on her hip, as she swept the dust, and worse, from our step, while my father helped those whose homes had been devastated – their possessions strewn all over the streets.

Of course, I do not remember that night. I only learnt of it later when my father told one of his tales, and even then I did not hold much importance to the Great Blowe; it was simply a piece of the history of my city, a tale told by old men. It was to be half a century later that I would come to realise how significant, for me and for my lunaticks, that great explosion had been.

In August 1648, as I toddled about our home, causing my own sort of destruction, our country was once again at war with itself. Rebellions in favour of the king broke out but were crushed in a matter of days by the forces of Oliver Cromwell, who then decided that England could never be settled in peace while Charles I remained alive. The king was charged with high treason, tried, found guilty, and beheaded at Whitehall, London, on the thirtieth day of January 1649. My father had been present, at the back of the crowd, and, years later, he told of how sickened he had been by the events of that awful day and the unrest that followed.

I have read many accounts of the rights and wrongs of that execution, but I still struggle to comprehend the true horror and uncertainty of those times, for, of course, I was just a baby, secure and happy in the arms of my mother, at the very centre of my beloved family.

THE RISE OF THE ORDINARY MAN

In the time that followed the Civil Wars, it became evident that the country was ready for a new system of power sharing, one based more on wealth and acquired power than family name and birthrights. Like many of his business associates and friends, now no longer held back by their lack of a title, my father's wealth grew – and so did his desire for power. He got his wish, for in the year that Charles I was beheaded, my father was elected sheriff of Norfolk, the principal law enforcer in the county. Then, in 1650, he became captain of the militia, a respected and prominent position, and his rise to the very top of political power in Norwich continued. My father enjoyed being a leader of men, with all the respect and regalia that came with it, and he started to behave accordingly, appearing to believe in his own 'greatness'. But, for all his outward pomp and bluster, my father was a generous man, and I still hear tales of his kind deeds, done quietly and with no need for show. Many remember him fondly for the good he did for the people of our fine city, some even believing that they owed my father a debt of gratitude. And several, thank the Lord, were able to repay that debt, many years later, when his nuisance of a daughter came calling with her crazy idea of building a hospital for the poor lunaticks in their city.

Despite his popularity, and prominence, my father still found time to add to his family, and another son and two more daughters had arrived by 1653, the first year of His Highness Oliver Cromwell, now Lord Protector of the Commonwealth of England. That same year, my father assumed the grandest of his titles, that of mayor of Norwich. He remained in high office throughout the time of the two Lord Protectors, firstly Oliver Cromwell, and then, after his death, his son Richard. But times and loyalties change. After eleven years without a king and uneasy with Cromwell's increasingly brutal policies, people were ready to give the monarchy another chance. In 1659, Richard Cromwell, a shy man with little desire to rule, was persuaded by the army to stand down, to be replaced by Charles II, the exiled son of the beheaded King Charles I.

Though quietly a supporter of Cromwell, at least in the early days of his rule, my father, too, was quite flexible in his loyalties when it suited him. Now an alderman, he was present when, on the tenth day of May 1661, King Charles II was solemnly proclaimed in Norwich. We once again had a king, and I can remember the bonfires and feasting that continued for days, as the country celebrated. My father was less impressed with all the fuss, '... perhaps the good people of Norwich were simply ready for a bit of a party...' I heard him mutter into his ale.

THE EXECUTION OF A DEAD MAN

In London, the new king, Charles II, had been restored to his throne, but he had not forgiven the death of his father. The twelve surviving participants in the trial and execution of Charles I were publicly hanged, drawn and quartered. And, as the laws of treason placed a traitor's remains at the king's disposal, he also ordered the posthumous execution of those traitors who were now deceased. Thus, the body of Oliver Cromwell was removed from Westminster Abbey, where he had been interred two years earlier following an extravagant funeral likened to that of a king. On the eleventh anniversary of the execution of King Charles I, Cromwell's remains were dragged through the streets of London in an open coffin, to the gallows, where he was hanged in full public view. At around four o'clock in the afternoon his body was taken down and his head put on a wooden spike and raised above Westminster Hall, the site of Charles I's trial. Within a few months, the king was crowned at Westminster, and, yes, my father found a reason to be present. Like many of those who had previously supported Cromwell, he was not against the new king; he was simply tired of wars and, along with most of the country, he prayed for peace.

A PRETTY YELLOW SONGBIRD

I grew through my childhood during years of uncertainty, but, as long as my family stayed safe and secure, I had little real cause to worry. Though my mother, surrounded by children, would sometimes explode with frustration at our antics, she was kind and loving, always trying to do the best for every one of us. And my father, well, he would make time for us, no matter how late he returned home – at least in the early days of his rise to power.

He made sure to use our birth names, quite a task with so many children, and he also created a pet name for each of us, reflecting a part of our character. His name for me was 'Mary Canary', named after the pretty yellow songbirds brought over by the Flemish weavers when they fled to Norwich from persecution in the Netherlands. The weavers had bred the birds, a reminder of their home, to keep them company as they worked their long days at their looms, and now many households throughout Norwich kept one in a little wooden cage. The canaries sang such a sweet song, but I know my father did not name me such because I had a sweet voice. Indeed, he would grimace if he came across me singing, and would make a point of looking behind the door, asking if one of the Yarmouth fishermen had moved into our house. And, as I glared at him, he would quickly call upon his politician's way with words and tell me he thought of me as his little canary because I was always so cheerful and optimistic, and nice to have around. Of course, this rather pleased me, though I made sure to sing particularly loudly whenever he was passing by.

Those pet names, however silly, were affectionately meant, and made us feel special. Simple enough perhaps, but something his own parents had neglected to do. My father would listen, with all seriousness, to our complicated ramblings, trivial little stories of our day, slights and fights against each other, and he managed to pay attention, to show us that our thoughts were important, and that he understood. And so, unburdened, we were free to skip away to get on with the rest of our day. And create yet more trouble for my poor mother.

TALES FROM STRANGER SHORES

My father loved to tell tales, tales that terrified and compelled us as we sat and listened and thrilled. Yet we also felt completely safe in our little world, snuggling close to our great protector, our father. My mother would be bustling around, always present to remind him to be careful, that we were too young to hear some of his more gruesome stories, often gleaned from travellers as they passed through our city. But, even so, he could sometimes be persuaded to tell us of the plays and performances, and the exotic animals he saw at the sideshows in the yard at the Angel

Inn – tales of lions, tigers, camels and jackals, and incredible feats performed by conjurers and acrobats from stranger shores. On occasion he might tell us of the more fearsome wonders he refused to let us see for ourselves, and we would have to make do with his words and our own imaginations – a hairy ape-child, a monstrous man who fed only on the roots of trees, and, of all things, a living skeleton.

My father was always careful to make sure my sensitive sister, Ellen, was not in the room when he told these tales, for fear of bringing on one of her hysterical attacks. But the rest of us, well, we loved his stories and the thrill of creating our own horrible images from his descriptions. When he realised he had said too much for our little ears, usually after a glare from my mother, my father would skilfully transform his story into something magical, a happier tale for us to take to bed, and to inhabit our dreams.

A RED WAND, A YARD AND A HALF LONG

As we grew older, we heard a little more of that dreadful summer in 1625 when the plague devastated our city, as seen through the eyes of my father, then a young man. We already knew some of the details from our older brothers, who were keen to show off their acquired knowledge, wanting to frighten us, with each tale becoming more gruesome the more it passed from mouth to mouth, from child to child. My father, like many who lived through that time, talked only rarely, and reluctantly, for his memories continued to haunt him, even decades later.

By far the worst memory for my father was when the bell-man, no longer merely calling the hour, warned everyone to put away their dogs and swine outside the city walls, on pain of being killed, for it was feared that those animals transmitted the plague. And his father had made him comply, taking all their dogs and their young and placing them with the other neighbourhood animals in a cart as it trawled the streets, children crying and shouting at the grim-faced cart-driver as he drove his whimpering load away.

My father also described the sorry sight of the infected poor being herded through the near-deserted streets, accompanied by a searcher holding a red wand, a yard and a half long, to the Black Tower, which had been made into pest houses. Everyone had known that those poor souls would never return to the city. They were walking to their place of death, taken away from their families, while their few pathetic possessions were loaded onto carts behind them to be burnt some miles away. They were watched at a distance by their neighbours, who held cloths seeped in lavender water close to their noses, in their belief that it would protect them from the plague. The streets remained quiet after they had passed, as if those who were well were ashamed to be ridding the city of the infected, but nevertheless accepting that it had to be done for the city to survive. And knowing that, if they showed signs of contagion, they, too, would be rounded up and taken away. The streets became even more terrifying after candle-lighting, deserted of the usual bustle of people, for they had all been warned to stay inside. As autumn descended, people sat at home and watched the early evenings darken. The fires, which had been lit to purify the air, only served to shroud the abandoned streets with their smoke.

'KISS MY ARSE'

One damp morning, after a heavy rain had flooded our usual route to church, we were forced to take a little-used path through an overgrown and deathly quiet street. We could see that most of the houses were deserted, boarded up, and we could just make out red crosses, the paint faded, on some of the doors. My father hurried us along, snapping at us to be silent, sharing a look with my mother, before he strode ahead. Later that evening my mother told us of how my father had grown up in that street, where the houses that had once been occupied by loving families were now locked up, abandoned by the living. Homes were left to decay and fall, no one wanting to live where that dreadful pestilence had visited with such vengeance – most occupants of those red-crossed houses now long dead.

We once saw my father shun a tired-looking gentleman as we passed through Tombland. This surprised us for my father was well known in the city and would frequently stop and exchange greetings with all sorts of people as we stood and waited, looking up at him. This old gentleman seemed nice, though his overcoat and shoes were a little shabby. He greeted my father warmly, as if he had known him as a boy. But my father abruptly passed him by, with a loud 'Kiss my arse' in response to the old man's hopeful, cautious greeting. Not understanding, and with my brothers stunned into silence at my father's outburst, I pestered my father to explain, but he just growled at me, and marched on so fast we had to scurry along to keep up with him. At home, once again we asked my mother, a safer person to question, what this poor old man had done to upset my father so. She sighed and quietly explained that there were a few people still living in the city who had survived the plague, but whose families had succumbed. This particular gentleman had tried to hide his daughter from the authorities when she had shown early signs of the infection. And when he spotted the first fatal black-green carbuncle on her pale, perfect skin, he had even tried to bribe one of the searchers, to buy their silence. But the searchers were made of sterner stuff – they had to be, to protect the city. His daughter had been found and taken to one of the pest houses, where she died, and the old man was condemned and shunned by his neighbours for risking the spread of that deadly disease. I felt so sad for that poor old man – he had lost his family and had been forced to move away, to the outskirts of the city, to live out his days alone. As we left the room, I turned to my sister, saying how unfair I thought it was, but my mother interrupted me and called us back. Speaking more loudly, she told us to remember that the plague years had been a harsh and cruel time, when most families suffered a loss and there were deaths every day. That man had risked the lives of all those who lived near him, and for that he should never be forgiven. Chastened, we silently crept away.

THAT SPOTTED DEATH

In 1665, when I was eighteen years old, war was proclaimed yet again, this time against the French. In London, there was another outbreak of plague, and the spread of that spotted death was only halted by a great fire that devastated the centre of the capital. In Norwich, as the first signs of contagion appeared, some of our leaders left for the safety of their country houses, but the mayor remained to ensure that the measures needed for the protection of his city were carried out. My father stayed too, and my mother refused to leave him, so we all stayed. We were not at risk, though, for, thanks to the hard work of my father, we lived in a large house, away from the cramped streets and poor living conditions that allowed the plague to thrive. We had good food, clean water and fresh air, and we were shielded from the worst of the sights that affected people in the poorer areas of Norwich, where more than two thousand people died.

It was a grim time for my father, yet he fully understood the seemingly cruel measures that had to be taken, for now he had his own family to protect. So, he helped to enforce the orders issued by the mayor, that the doors of the dwellings of all persons that had died of the infection should be nailed up and watched, their families nailed up inside with the corpse until they, too, died. I also heard of the order that any person found begging in the street was to be whipped. This struck me as being quite uncharitable, as if the poor wretches had any choice at all – to starve or be whipped. I carelessly made that comment to my father after the plague had abated, and I remember it as the one time that he truly snapped at me. He stood up from his chair and paced, then said, almost to himself, that I had to understand that all our loved ones, and the people in our city, had survived simply because of those cruel measures. It had been brutal, but it had been the only way to halt the spread of that unforgiving disease. My father, ranting now as I had never seen him before, went on about the courage of the mayor, how he had the strength to act, to enforce the orders of the king, though he knew it would make him unpopular with some. And then, more gently, but looking straight at me, so I could not avoid his eyes, my father said, 'Sometimes, Mary, doing your duty can make you unpopular but if you truly believe you can act for the greater good, then you must be strong, and believe in God's purpose…' Pausing, then, as if to say more, he took a breath then turned and left me, and strode towards the Angel.

A BEQUEST TO NORWICH LIBRARY

To give him his due, my father, a rich and powerful man, was not only seeking mere wealth and influence, he also recognised the importance of education and culture. He made sure we could all read and he employed tutors to teach us to write. He once found me in a quiet corner of our garden reading one of the pamphlets that circulated, full of news from the wider world and the new developments in science and medicine, and he remarked: 'So, Mary Canary, is that where you get all your clever ideas from?' My father, he who had raised me, in a house full of his books, did he not think I was curious for more, or that I was incapable of picking up a pamphlet? Or, the Lord forbid, perhaps even to write one? But of course, now I have reason to thank my father's foresight, for he thought to educate his daughters as well as his sons, which was unusual for our times, and I am forever grateful for the benefit it gave me in my later years. My father could see the advantage that education gave to those who were fortunate enough to receive it. He had met a young man called Samuel Chapman from Corpus Christi College in Cambridge, who had benefited from a scholarship, and was planning to bequest funds for the maintenance of other poor scholars at the college. Their meeting prompted my father to donate many of his books for the benefit of Norwich Library. My father was impressed that this Samuel Chapman had specified that his scholarship should be used for needy scholars with no importance given to their names or family influence. His act of benevolence suited my father's politics and so began a friendship between the two men that lasted until his death.

THIS LOVELY MAN

I had reason to notice this man, Samuel Chapman, some years later, when he came to visit my father for supper, after attending a meeting at Norwich Library, at the New Hall, close to our house. I was a little taken aback as he strode in, bringing with him a scent of wood smoke and rosemary, and I stood, like a fool, taking all of him in. A gentle nudge from my father reminded me of my manners, and I forced a polite, though stuttered, greeting. I could not believe that this man, this lovely man, was the same person that my father had been talking of when he droned on about scholars and bequests. I clearly should have paid more attention. I watched him as he carefully washed his hands before our meal, and noticed, later, how he slowly moved his hands to his face to gently smell the rosemary oil I had infused into the soap. I started to move around the table to get closer to him, discreetly, I felt, but my father was not to be fooled, and suggested, with a small smile, that I should commence serving the meal. I chose not to hear him, but as I moved closer to the door, closer to this man, in popped an annoyance in lace, and she was introduced as his new wife. I was not keen. She was pretty, if you like that sort of thing, and he seemed to like her, I could see that. But I could not comprehend that sensible, learned men could be taken in by flounce and frills. Were all men really such fools? Sadly, and rather disappointingly, it appeared to be so, for even my father had become a little flushed and sweaty when she turned her attention on him.

As they fussed around her, I took the opportunity to dampen my handkerchief with cool water, and pressed it to my neck and throat, as I suddenly realised that I desired this man, of all the men I had ever met. And then, as I watched them together, I wished that he would look at me that way, entranced, almost – but I was not pretty, and I dressed plainly, for God cares not. I knew I was quite unremarkable and outwardly serious and could not compete with his fancy wife. Still, I couldn't help but hope that, if he glanced at me at all, he would not simply see a dutiful daughter, an unmarried spinster. No, I wished that he could see me as I truly was – that he could glimpse the longing in my passionate heart.

As the meal dragged on, I was at least able to be solicitous towards them, though I was pleased to see that this wife creature greedily had a full share of the roots I had boiled, and I was undone enough by the very presence of this man to hope that they caused her wind. I noticed, too, as I sat directly across from him, that he had devoured a great plate of our succulent beef with evident relish.

The men became engrossed in a serious conversation about the Norwich Library and some of the great books there. One of the precious volumes from my father's library, Thomas Browne's *Urne Burial* had somehow made its way into my possession, and I had been reading and absorbing its contents at night as my candle burnt low. As they talked, I suddenly looked up from my plate and exclaimed, 'Life is a pure flame, and we live by an invisible sun within us…' then I faltered as they all turned to look at me, with what I presumed to be amusement, and I was struck silent for the remainder of the meal.

As he took his leave, after thanking me for the efforts I had taken with the supper, that lovely man turned to my father and said that he recommended Thomas Browne's *Religio Medici* for his ideas about science and religion. The following day, my father placed his own copy of that book in my hands, and, though he made no comment, he raised an eyebrow, and as he turned away I saw the glimmer of a smile. Years later, he told me that it had been one of his proudest moments, to have raised such a daughter, even one who dressed plainly and shunned pretty lace collars.

Later that night, I brushed out my hair, my one vanity, which was usually hidden under a plain cap but which, when let loose, reached thickly down my back. I paused in my hundred strokes and imagined that lovely man carefully gathering my hair in his hands and pulling me close to him. I had that picture strong in my mind, though I had no idea of what would happen next. Annoyingly, despite my desires and my best efforts, I was never at home when he called to visit my father, and it was many years before I even saw him again. But at night I often closed my eyes and imagined his strong hands gently entwined in my hair…

A BLAZING STAR

My father, who had started life as a tailor's apprentice, remember, had risen to become one of the most powerful men in Norwich and enjoyed being the centre of attention in all the city's ceremonies and celebrations. But whatever velvet gown and decoration my father was now entitled to wear, and however many aldermen and sheriffs he presided over, most of all my father simply loved to talk. He continued to visit the Angel Inn, still fond of their ales and acquiring a taste for their brandy, though now he used his time there to talk politics and to form allegiances.

My father was primarily successful in business because of his solid reputation for quality and good service. He already had his loyal and regular customers, and, after the restoration of Charles II, when the rich and favoured were ready for a period of flamboyance, and the demand for luxurious cloth and exquisite clothes was high, my father was well prepared. He had used his political power to strengthen his contacts within Norfolk, particularly with the worsted weavers, and had a steady supply of high-quality cloth just when he needed it. He was able to meet the demands of the great and the rich in London, and even of the lower classes, who followed the new fashions whenever they could afford it. He was not alone – all the other prominent men in our city recognised this new beginning, and, more importantly, the opportunities afforded by this flamboyant king and his love of the good life. Those were golden times for my father. One December evening, we watched as a blazing star lit a path across the sky after sunset, with the tail reaching far towards the east, and my father, content with his lot, and after an ale or three, joked that he was also a blazing star, spreading his influence throughout Norwich, where he was reputed to be the 'richest man in town'. That was my father. The great John Mann. A star indeed.

My favourite memory of him, though, was when a travelling show with a pair of elephants came to the Angel in 1685. We reminded my father of the fanciful tales he had told us as children when we had been deemed too young to see for ourselves the marvels and monstrosities he described. Now we were adults, and he had no option but to organise an outing for all of us to see this famed show. My father was getting old, and a little unsteady, but he was always ready to go out and about and didn't hesitate to use his connections to ensure we had a first-hand view. I accompanied him, my brothers and their wives, to see those wondrous creatures, God's creations. And that is the image I keep of my father, not in his finery off to meet the king, but at the Angel that day, with his family nearby, and at the centre of his friends, in his city, talking, telling tales, laughing and loving his life.

Three

'IT HATH PLEASED ALMIGHTY GOD TO VISIT SOME OF MY NEAREST RELATIONS AND KINDRED WITH LUNACY'

I have been told I was a lively little girl, adept at organising people and getting my own way. I would chatter on about this or that, always with something vitally important to say, though I could be struck silent in front of visitors to our house, when my confidence would desert me. I would try to do kindly deeds, maybe pick a few flowers from the garden, and leave them on the doorstep for my mother to find, or I would ask her for some small tasks, to help her out, to make her smile. But behind my sunny appearance I would also find time to plot some sort of mischief. My favourite trick usually involved frogs, which I adored. I made little homes for them in the corner of our garden, so I could always have one on hand when required. I even put some young frogs into a little-used drawer in the cabinet in our living room, but, of course, being frogs, they escaped, causing my mother's kitchen maid to scream for quite some time. As I scurried to recapture them all, it was clear that it was not one of my better ideas. I used my frogs to torment my horrible brothers, as payback for the times they had upset my younger sister, dearest Ellen, who even then was rather delicate. A frog would put in an appearance at odd times, when they were least expecting it, in a shoe perhaps, or a pocket, or their hat. Of course, I was never suspected, I was far too sweet in those days, and, of course, a girl would never keep frogs. It was usually another one of my brothers who got the blame, and his protestations only got him into more trouble, which I felt was a well-executed plan, all told. And my frog would be quietly and gently removed by me amidst all the fuss, returned to his damp little home and rewarded with some succulent slugs that I plucked from our vegetable garden.

It has always seemed strange to me that I had been such a cheery child, but that as I grew older I had, for a time at least, become a serious young woman, though still secure in the love of my family and devoted to my faith. My mother used to tease me, admonish me, try to persuade me to take life less seriously, to have more fun. But I could never be completely carefree. I was all too aware even at a young age of the suffering and inequality that I could see all around me. I used to wonder at my two older sisters' ability to ignore others' hardships, how they could laugh and delight in such trivial things as pretty dresses, trinkets or the sly glances of the pushy young apprentices who worked for my father. That was not for me, but I was not unhappy, just more serious than a girl from such a loving and fortunate family ought to be. It was as though I was constantly aware of the danger, the possibility, that the family I loved so dearly could be lost at any moment.

FLOWERS ON A DOORSTEP

For a while I tried to be more carefree, to join in with my sisters, though I found most of their conversations downright silly, and they could sense that I wasn't really part of their little world. I continued to be careful, in my speech and actions, not wishing to upset anyone, my mother least of all. Still, as I grew through my teen years, I did start to believe that my family would stay safe, under the watchful guard of my father and the protective care of my mother. I took to washing my hair each week, brushing it patiently whilst it dried in the sun or by the heat of the fire, much to the amusement of my older sisters, who, being in possession of pretty faces, did not see the need. They would sometimes follow me about, and chant, quietly so that only I could hear, 'Meek and mild, Mary Mann, will bear no child, nor tempt a man'. I ignored them as best I could, and, despite their meanness, started to have occasional thoughts of how it might be to have the attentions of a young man, to be a wife, a mother. I chanced to dream little contented dreams of having my own family to nurture. So, of course, my world crashed in on me with all its might when my beloved mother died unexpectedly, and bloodily, in 1667, when I was twenty years old.

My mother had taken a basket of provisions to a pitiful family decimated by consumption, and soon after she had shown the terrible signs of infection herself: the chills, the weakness, and then the blood. My father kept us away, fearing the disease would spread, and she quickly succumbed, with only my father beside her, in her final hours. It was as though everything I had most feared throughout my childhood had now come true. Over the next few months I existed in a state of anxious dread, though nobody noticed, for outwardly I was calm, capable Mary, helping others, doing my duty, upsetting no one.

After my mother's death, my father moved away for a time until he was sure that he did not carry the infection, and as the most sensible daughter I took on her motherly duties. My older sisters were preparing to marry and leave home and laughed off my quiet requests for their help, and as for my brothers, well, I knew it was pointless trying to persuade them to do anything. My father, who had been married to my mother for twenty-nine years, was so distraught that he was unable to understand anyone's loss except his own. I tried, once, as I took him another mug of ale, to ask him to make my sisters take their share of the household duties, but as I approached him, my arguments fully prepared, he looked up at me, his face mottled and his eyes bloodshot and wet, and I was unable to speak. To spare him any more distress I did not talk of my own sadness, and I, alone, took on the day-to-day care of the younger children whilst my older sisters, with their fickle complexions, were free to wail out their grief, and my brothers simply carried on as if nothing had happened.

And then I had to consider my younger sister, desperate and in need of care. My poor dear sister Ellen, who had suffered for most of her life from the most distressing mental torments, and who had needed at those times constant care by a familiar person, most usually my mother, whose calm presence I now, somehow, had to replace. Ellen was wholly unable to understand my mother's absence. Aiming for comfort but causing distress, my father had decreed that Ellen was not to see my mother's cold dead body, which had been spirited away in the hour after her death. But Ellen could not comprehend that her protector, our mother, had left her, and she was too agitated to make sense of our muddled words of explanation.

Our mother's sudden absence triggered one of Ellen's most disturbed episodes, and she became beyond reason. She howled and screamed for hours, taking every chance to harm herself and refusing all our attempts to console her. Anything she could reach – pillows, shoes, even the bedwarmer and my precious Bible – were thrown at the door to our room, to repel anyone who dared try and enter. Fortunately, Ellen and I shared the bedchamber at the end of the hallway and no one needed to pass through to get to their own sleeping room. We moved the little ones out, for they were quite fearful of their now completely deranged sister. My older sisters were most put out at having to share their space with the troublesome little children and didn't even attempt to disguise their annoyance. But, tired of their self-centred complaints, and with no one to speak up for me, I firmly and quite loudly insisted that they had no choice. I was shaking a little as I waited for their response, but they were so shocked that I, little meek and mild Mary, had spoken out, they made no more objections. And that was that. Then I watched Ellen, taking every chance to dart into our room to remove anything she might use to harm herself – and to rescue my little collection of books and pamphlets, hidden under the bed. And, well, I waited. Eventually, and quite abruptly, she quietened. With a feeling of dread, I opened the door to our room, and I could see her on the bed, perfectly still. I moved slowly, gently, towards her and she looked up at me, distant and defeated. I reached out to take her hand, but she shrank away. So, I simply stayed with her, for hours, then for days. My attempts to talk were met with a dark glare, so I kept my distance. But I did not go far away. I left small nibbles of cheese, fresh bread and sweet biscuits to tempt her, and an old mug filled with weak ale by her bed, and in time these needed to be replenished and her pot needed to be emptied. Slowly, she accepted that our mother had gone, and that she would have to make do with me, a poor replacement, but, grudgingly, she grew to tolerate my presence. Over many months, Ellen had more periods of distress, and during her worst times I was quite unable to leave her side, always having to be close to her, to reassure and protect her as best I could from her inner turmoil.

As I sat with Ellen, trying to read but unable to concentrate fully on the words in front of me, her sadness reminded me that my poor mother had suffered, too, in the years leading up to her death. I recalled how she had lost her vitality, and seemed somehow dulled, yet she still retained enough strength to care for us and to hide her despair from my father. She never recovered, I think, from the deaths of her last two children, little Becky, who was born small and sickly and died at just a few months old, and then Timothy, who somehow survived his traumatic birth only to succumb, unexpectedly, in the days before his first birthday. And so my mother began her decline into an overwhelming sadness. Maybe she was just worn out, or maybe she could not bear to suffer such loss again. Whatever, she would have no more children and a gentle melancholy settled over her for the remaining years of her life. For ten long, sad years. I recall one evening, when my mother, tired of the world, had once again taken herself off to bed, I heard my father talking to my brother, saying, '… she has lost so many… over the years…' Of course, I was just ten years old, a child, when Timothy died, and I did not understand what my father meant. Now, though, it is clear she had suffered other losses; they both had. I am glad of my father's understanding, but at the time it felt like I was the only one who could see how my mother had changed. After only a short period of mourning for little Timmy, for he had died so young, and even less time for poor Becky, the rest of the household, caught up in their own lives, carried on as usual. My father's wealth had at least provided my mother with some comfort, for he had insisted that both babies were buried in coffins made to his specifications, and each had their own tiny grave. The children of the great John Mann would not be placed in the coffin of another, as was the way for children of the poor.

I could sense my mother's lasting anguish, and I made sure to spend more time with her, finding an excuse to show her some little thing, a reason to talk, to pretend that all was well. I would pick a handful of lavender, knowing that she loved the scent, like those times in my childhood when I would leave a pretty flower on the doorstep for her to find. I was always looking, I suppose, for a glimpse of the mother who had gone. And, though she was always kind and still loving with us, her joy of life was gone, and her feisty personality was dampened, and then extinguished.

My father, trying his best to make my mother happy, and at a loss to know what to say, had bought her a pretty yellow canary, with green tips on its wings, in an exquisite cage of mahogany and brass, with two porcelain bowls. And, though I think he understood that expensive gifts could not help her, still he would hope, picking up the cage to move the bird into whichever room my mother was in, so that she could hear its sweet chirruping. And she would look at him and smile, her eyes filled with sad tears at his kindness.

A few months after my mother's death, when Ellen had calmed and had begun to eat her meals with us once again, the canary was still singing its bright and cheerful tunes, though no one bothered to move it from room to room any more. One morning I came into the parlour to see Ellen holding the cage, its door ajar, next to an open window. She looked at me, but I simply nodded as she let the little bird fly away, for I, too, could no longer bear to hear its happy little songs.

Two years later, the city suffered the spread of another pestilence, this time of smallpox, which raged and devastated more than 300 families in just a fortnight. Again, we all survived. My father was living a good life, though perhaps he was lonely. He had been shattered by the loss of my mother, for his great love and life partner had been taken from him. He remained alone for two years after her death, far longer than was expected of a widower in those times, when a wife was considered essential to all men of means.

Eventually, following a brief courtship, my father remarried. His new wife, at just twenty years old, was a little younger than me, and my father was in his seventh decade. It was not the loving partnership that he had had with my mother, but they were amicable enough, perhaps more than amicable for there was certainly something in their marriage that seemed to suit them both. His new wife was called Dorothy and I thought perhaps we could be friends. My older sisters had left home by then, though I can't say I missed them too much, and I welcomed some female company for, as much as I loved Ellen, her condition at that time meant that she could not offer me real friendship. Dorothy was gentle and quiet, and gave my father no argument or dissent, and, at first, I could not see her appeal. Though, given that my mother, God rest her, and most of his children by her were all rather strong-willed, perhaps my father now sought a less demanding time towards the end of his life. Dorothy fitted easily into our lives and I did not think to resent her for she was clearly so very different from our darling mother. All around us I saw that, as wives and husbands died, people looked for companionship and often remarried quickly. I accepted that was simply what happened in the round of life. Dorothy was at least a welcome help to me, taking a share of caring for the younger children so that I had time to sit with my Ellen during the worst of her fits of hysteria and bouts of melancholy. The little ones certainly preferred Dorothy; she had a way of making chores fun and they would do her bidding without the noisy protest and tantrums they often reserved for me.

Dorothy was clearly uneasy in the presence of my sister and would often leave the room when she entered. Having grown up with Ellen and watched the calm way my mother behaved with her, I could see that even the worst of her hysterical fits, though quite frightening to an outsider, were at least predictable. I knew that eventually Ellen would wear herself out and become calm, whereas I found managing our noisy little rabble day after day, particularly when they were overtired, a more tiresome task. Dorothy organised the little ones and I sat with Ellen. It was an arrangement that suited all of us. I was glad of Dorothy's presence, though I had become a little irritated with her; she had so little to say for herself and behaved as if she were in complete awe of my father, who, though I loved him dearly, was still just a man, despite all his wealth and titles. Dorothy and I found a way to more or less get along. No great friendship, but no arguments or drama either. And I was grateful for that. But then I came to see another side of her.

One afternoon Dorothy and I were in our little garden and I was chatting away (more to fill the silence than anything), and I was explaining about the different herbs that grew there – how I would use pot marigold to prepare a tonic to soothe Ellen and add camomile to a salve to stop her scratching at her sore, dry hands. I paused, a little impatient at having to always lead a conversation, and I noticed that Dorothy was kneeling down and gently picking the bright flowers, looking at each one before placing it in her lap.

Then she started to speak, hesitantly and quietly at first, as though to herself. I began to cut some of the herbs around me, far more than I needed but as a distraction, just so that she would continue to talk. She confided that, though she loved our little ones, she was somewhat overwhelmed by taking on so many step-children. At just twenty years old, she was daunted by having to entertain in my father's absence, and act as the head of the household when my older brothers and their wives came to visit. She talked of how she had moved away from life in a village to come to this great city. How she had left her beloved mother and was suddenly expected to be a wife, mother, housekeeper: a grown woman, with all that that entailed. She drifted into silence, and then, for the first time, I spoke of the loss that occupied my thoughts each and every day, my fear of living my life without my own mother beside me, without her to guide me. And Dorothy simply sat and listened, glancing up at me as I talked, and I was touched by her attention. Feeling a little more kindly towards her, I thought of how young Dorothy was to take on so many responsibilities, how she was expected to be a wife to this important man, and step-mother to his rowdy, self-confident family. She talked more of her own family, her childhood, and a little unexpectedly, of her devotion to my father. We once again lapsed into silence, though we continued to cut back the herbs and take out the weeds for some time, in a lovely shared peace. We had a little more understanding of each other after that, and I was able to treat her with more patience, though I was rarely able to coax much laughter from her; she remained a most serious young wife.

There was one aspect of her life with my father that I certainly did not discuss with Dorothy, and that was how she had tamed my father's desire to have more children. She had managed to keep to just one child by him, born a year after they were married – we called her 'the little one', Dottie. Although Dottie's birth was straightforward, and I could see that Dorothy clearly doted on her little daughter, there were no more children. Sometimes I wondered if Dorothy had found a way to stop further pregnancies. I heard her talking quietly, even secretly, with the few friends she had made, also new mothers, so perhaps there was a way that women knew, and told each other, of how to avoid conceiving more children. Dorothy was so devout I am sure she would have known that to somehow guard against having children was regarded as a sin. Mind, I could hear her regularly with my father, through the walls, so I am sure they did not practise abstinence. It appears there was much I did not understand about the lives of women. My own sisters, both married and with children, always excluded me from such talk, though that was much to my relief, in some ways.

My mother's love of children was strong in me, and how I longed for my own little child. It seemed unlikely to ever happen, given my life and my responsibilities, but I prayed that one day I would be blessed. I suppose it was easier to simply accept that while my life was not complicated by the presence of a husband or my own little ones, I could use all my strength to care for those who needed me. I trusted in God and looked to the future.

I tried to accept that it had pleased Almighty God to visit some of my nearest relations and kindred with lunacy, and I did my utmost to offer them kindness and gentle care. Sadly, there were many in our city who had no compassion for the suffering of lunaticks, believing it to be a punishment from God for some unknown wrongdoing. I had even had to protect my darling Ellen, who would cause harm to no one, from the jeers of the rabble, as she quietly went about her business. I recall one particularly dreadful day, after I had persuaded her to join me on a quick trip to the bookseller near the Guild Hall, when she had suddenly become overwhelmed by the throng of people in the marketplace – running into the nearest shop looking for a place to hide, while I followed closely behind, apologising to the people she pushed out of her way. Fortunately, the shopkeeper recognised us, and he tried to be sympathetic, though I'm sure I saw him smirk as I tried to coax poor Ellen out from behind the counter. The other customers stood and watched, and seemed to find her panicked state amusing, moving slowly out of the way as, eventually, I was able to gently guide her outside. We were confronted by more people who had been attracted by the commotion, and, as they stared and spat at us, I had to pull our shawls over our heads and hurry Ellen away, looking for the safety of home.

My father, seeing the state of us on our return, was livid, and he immediately marched to the marketplace but, of course, the crowd had dispersed, and the shopkeeper and his customers innocently expressed concern and behaved with perfect respect in his presence. I regretted not turning to confront the bullies who had taunted her, though I now know that merely shaming them would not change their views of the mad; I understood their fear, but I could not forgive their cruelty. Ellen looked, as many lunaticks do, unremarkable, most of the time, and, hence, the sudden onset of her hysterical behaviour could be quite shocking to those with little experience of caring for the distracted. And perhaps that is the whole problem: people can't always see the illness that inhabits the minds of the mad.

It still makes me furious to see the ignorant, and the cruel, mocking the poor lunaticks who live on the streets of Norwich, picking on those who have no one to protect them. The servant of one of the quacks peddling his false potions from a stall in the market was one of the worst. He was a most vicious man, with a loud and foul voice, always jesting about some poor soul or other in the crowd around their stall, all to draw attention to his master's wares, of course. And some people even joined in with his jeering, for most of them had not the strength of character to walk away. Eventually, enough good people did complain about the obscenity of his speech, and he was removed from the city. But he was not the only one to deliver such cruel abuse. The mad folk and natural-born idiots are still regularly subjected to horrendous physical attacks, simply because they are alone, vulnerable and, of course, different. I am reminded of a passage from the good book: 'Who maketh thee to differ from another?' Who indeed? I would be greatly pleased if more of those who cast their insults would acquaint themselves with the words of our Lord.

WHEN LUNACY IS UPON HER

Perhaps I should tell more of the torments of my poor sister, Ellen. My mother said she was a delicate little thing from birth, always keeping close and quite unable to separate from her as she grew older, as most children do. Never wanting to be out and about in the world, never in trouble, but unable to experience joy. Whereas I just didn't see the point in most of the activities that were considered fun by others, and I certainly preferred my own company to that of the twittering girls who came to visit my older sisters, and who talked about nothing I considered worthy at all. But I could still enjoy a beautiful day or appreciate the scent of the wildflowers growing in amongst the vegetables in our garden, whilst Ellen took no pleasure in most of life. She would eat because she had to but derived little delight from it, even when my father brought little fancies to tempt her. She could be persuaded to dress nicely when we had guests, but she did not seem to notice the fine fabrics or delicate embroidery produced by my father's tailors. In truth, Ellen was only ever fully content when she had my mother's whole attention, perhaps sitting quietly together in our garden while the rest of the family were elsewhere. She would create such a fuss if she ever lost sight of my mother, and, after a few attempts at leaving her with my older sisters, our mother, seeing that it was kinder, made sure to stay close by. My father understood that Ellen wasn't being spoilt or behaving badly when she had her fits. It was just the way she was, and no words or punishment would cure her. Ellen showed no jealousy and tolerated my mother's pregnancies. When, growing big and slow, my mother spent most of her time just sitting, Ellen would be next to her, content and calm. After the babies were born, Ellen simply stayed close to each one, helping to gently hold them, knowing that, wherever the new baby was, my mother would always be nearby too.

Of all her sisters, Ellen preferred me, or at least she tolerated me the most. We were close in age and as she grew older she would sometimes spend a little time in my company, though always with the reassurance of my mother's return. At night, as we lay in the dark, waiting for sleep, Ellen would ask me to talk to her, to tell her of my day, to distract her from her dread of dark silence. For all the years we shared a sleeping room, I can't recall ever seeing her in a deep sleep. In the long winter nights, whenever I awoke from my first sleep, I would feel Ellen's eyes resting on me, and then she would cautiously ask a question, seemingly prepared as if she had been waiting for me, and we would talk once more, over the heads of the little ones squashed between us. It could be any little thing, just to get me talking again, to keep her company until the morning, when she could resume her attendance on my mother.

My father and mother had always hoped, and I heard them pray, that Ellen would grow out of her clinginess, but as she reached her teenage years her anxieties became worse and she refused to leave the house at all. My father asked a renowned minister, visiting from London, to see Ellen to offer his opinion. But the minister started to look for signs of possession in her, for evidence of evil spirits, and my father, knowing my sister, knowing her goodness of spirit, politely, but decisively, moved the minister towards the door. My father also consulted a respected physician who, with only a brief glance at Ellen (such was his expertise), advised that her symptoms were common in young women and would pass when she began her monthly bleeds. But, when that time came, Ellen did not lessen her devotion to my mother, nor did she become any more sociable or tolerant of visitors. Another physician, noting my sister's pale complexion, promptly diagnosed chlorosis or green-sickness. When he had gone, my mother firmly stated her opinion that Ellen's pale skin was due to her being housebound most of the time, rather than to any illness. My father nodded his agreement, and the diagnosis of this supposed expert medical man was also promptly discounted and his costly physick poured away. Over the years numerous doctors developed various theories for the cause of Ellen's distress and some even advised purging and bleeding, which my father refused; simply by looking at his daughter he knew it would do her no good and he was unwilling to subject her to further torments. How I loved him for that decision, for that strength.

Throughout my life I have argued against the common belief that it was God's will to subject Ellen, and others, to the agonies of their minds as punishment for some wrongdoing. I admit that I find it hard to reconcile His purpose in creating such suffering with my belief in His wisdom, yet I have continued to offer my thankfulness to Him, for blessing me with the use of my reason and understanding. For this invaluable mercy, I have endeavoured to offer comfort and protection to those in distress. Whenever I was tempted by thoughts of another life, I thought of the gift He had bestowed upon me. God had called me to care for those in need and if I faltered, I reminded myself, 'All is the Lord's'. All of my mind, and all of my life, it seemed.

STICKS AND STONES

I had to remind myself of God's wisdom, once more, after hearing of an untimely and tragic death. A young man had slipped and fallen into the bleak and icy River Wensum. It had been reported officially as an accident, but I overheard my father telling Dorothy that a passer-by had seen the poor boy, albeit at some distance, in apparent distress, removing all his clothes as he stumbled along the top of the bridge, near to where he was found. They hesitated to tell me of his death, and I was shocked to learn that it was a boy we used to know. He was one of a troublesome little troop of children that frequented our streets in the good weather, though he would mostly just tag along after them, trying to be friends. He would usually get left behind or, if he was not taken with their plan for the day, he would simply turn around and walk home alone. Even when the other children grew tired of his odd behaviour and repetitive chanting, and told him to go away, it did not appear to bother him, and he would usually come and seek me out instead. He was happiest if he found me alone in our garden, where we would sit and use stones to make intricate patterns in the soil, designs that were quite beautiful as they wound around the roses. I could see that this occupied him and kept him happy, and I, too, filled my thoughts with the trails we created. I was young and unaware that I was being kind, but, as I look back, I can see that I was showing a patience that would serve me well in my later dealings with the disturbed. But my father recognised then that my compassion was unusual in such a young child, and perhaps that was why, in later years, he assigned me as a carer to those in need amongst our kin. Sometimes, when the plight of the mad starts to trouble me more than usual, I wish I had shown a flair for something else, something simple, needlework perhaps, or looking pretty. Or any other of the skills possessed by the young women my mother had half-heartedly tried to persuade me to mix with. She had little success with that, I hasten to add, and thankfully she soon gave up.

THE ARRIVAL OF NATHANIEL MANN

As if I was not quite busy enough, I was also called upon by my father to care for his brother, Nathaniel Mann. My father had not seen him for many years as Nathaniel had, like my father, left home at the first opportunity, declining all contact with his parents and his many brothers and sisters. He had become a most godly pastor, in a town outside Norwich, but over the years the Reverend Nathaniel Mann had declined into a deep melancholic state, often to the brink of suicide. He managed for a while to stay in his lodgings, when, it was recorded, 'Many prayers were put up to God for him, and many made to God with him, and he himself was almost always alone upon his knees.' Eventually his condition deteriorated further, and, though there were many who would pray with him, there were none who had the means to care for him. A small group of his former parishioners had brought him to Norwich. They simply left him at the door of his brother, the illustrious and benevolent John Mann, who had no choice but to take him in, and benevolently we made room in our crowded house. Nathaniel was little trouble for a while, but then his emotional disorder worsened and he needed to be watched constantly. And, of course, that duty fell to me, the very kind, and very put-upon, Mary Mann.

I was unsure of caring for this man, as he was a different type of lunatick to my sister, whom I had grown up with and grown used to. He seemed to be rather too interested in me, and he definitely had too many hands. I tried to speak to my father, but he was preoccupied with the visit of King Charles to Norwich and just asked that I be a little more patient until the reverend settled in. Unable, yet again, to argue against my father, I found my own way of dealing with the mad wandering hands by keeping ever watchful and never passing too close to him, and, on the occasions that I had to bathe him, I found that a cold wash cloth was quite effective if he overstepped the mark.

When Ellen's condition deteriorated too, and I was quite torn between the two lunaticks, my father finally accepted something had to be done and he arranged for Nathaniel to share a lodging close to our house, with a family of Strangers. The 'Strangers' were a large population of migrants from the Netherlands, who had come to Norwich a hundred or so years before to escape persecution in their own country. They were expert weavers and hard workers, and kept to their own areas, building up little communities and worshipping at their own churches. At one time they made up almost a third of the people in our city, though some had since returned home. The good and mostly tolerant folk of Norwich had welcomed them, as they recognised skilled workers and could see the benefits their industry could bring to our city. My father and the other tailors had built up contact with these Strangers, eager to harness their skills with the loom. And this particular family were happy to take into their care the brother of the great and respected John Mann, who had put much work their way. They had put an extra pallet bed in one of their outbuildings, a dry and comfortable sleeping room, which was occupied by another distracted soul, their aged father, who, thankfully, paid no attention to the reverend's constant praying. The place was clean, for the old man kept himself busy all day sweeping the floor of the outbuilding with a broom that he rarely put down. The reverend was able to continue praying, even whilst making way for the old man's broom every so often. He asked me to take some lavender that he could throw on the floor to sweeten the air, and which gave his companion something else to sweep for a while, leaving Nathaniel free to pray in peace. They kept warm with a fire that, despite their madness, they managed well. The two men formed a sort of friendship, which was tolerable to them both, and as the years passed the Lord graciously granted Nathaniel some periods of relief from his distress.

I called in daily, and they were always waiting for me at their door to see which one of my herbal remedies or tonics I had brought. They were both partial to a peppery hyssop tisane that they were certain soothed their coughs and sore throats. In the colder months I would take an ointment made from bay to ease their stiff joints. And I would always deliver some pottage and extra bread from our kitchen, much to their pleasure. The reverend settled into his new home and thereafter required no extra attention from us beyond my daily supplies, and the occasional book that I purchased from the market. Indeed, for some years before he died, he did little else but read and pray. At the last he died the ordinary death of men, and, quietly, in his bed, he surrendered up his soul to God.

MY KINDRED

My father, while rarely talking of my mother after her death, or considering the effect her loss may have had on the rest of the family, did at least acknowledge my sacrifice. On returning from the Angel Inn one night, finding me sitting up with Ellen and praying with her that she might rest, he paused at the door, swaying a little, and commented, with a soft smile, 'My Mary, I thank God that our poor Ellen has you. How would we ever manage if you were to leave us?' I was pleased he had found it in himself to put that into words, but I would have liked him instead to talk of finding me a suitor, so that my life could begin. I wanted to speak out that night, to tell him of my loneliness, but I knew it was impossible, for my family truly would not have been able to manage without me. As he moved towards the stairs, I simply uttered a quiet 'Good-night' and turned back to my Bible. But what else could I do? Have Ellen turned out on the streets with the other unfortunates? Of course not. We knew of no decent hospitals for the treatment of those affected by lunacy, and, even if there had been, we all knew that Ellen would not survive being separated from us. And what of Nathaniel, whom my father appeared to have forgotten about? I was aware that without the kindness of his parishioners, who had brought him to our home, Nathaniel would have been left to roam the lanes of our county, alone with his prayers, until some dreadful accident would likely have ended his days on earth. I am satisfied that at least we found him a place of ease and safety in his final years.

I saw so many poor, distressed people every day within our city. Some of them, at least those with loving families, were well cared for in their own homes. Some, whose families could not accept their distress, were hidden away. And where the family was wealthy, if not particularly charitable, people were put in a private hospital (not that this guaranteed any form of treatment or even decent care), often to be forgotten. In the severest of cases, when the private hospitals refused to admit the particularly disturbed, I heard of people being taken to a strange city by their kin and turned out on the streets to take their chances, alone in this brutal and cruel world. And, even while thinking over my father's well-meant words and regretting that I hadn't spoken up, I knew I really had no other choice but to continue to do my duty to my kindred.

'THE MAD LOVER'

There was a place we had heard of, where lunaticks were locked away. It was called the Bethlehem Hospital in London, but such was its reputation for harbouring the most incurable of lunaticks, and for its cruelty, it was known as the Bedlam. We did not know whether to believe the tales of the poor souls behind its doors, being goaded and poked with sticks to enrage them, solely for the entertainment of visitors. I liked to think that people would not behave that way, but then my father, perhaps to try and unburden himself of his knowledge, told me of his own experience of that dreadful place.

He had returned late one afternoon from a visit to his tailors' shops in London. We all welcomed him back joyfully, and Dorothy, who was still young enough to show her excitement, hugged him as he produced a gift for each of us. From his bag he took a silver-backed hairbrush for Dorothy, a cushion of the softest velvet for Ellen, and little trinkets and gewgaws for the little ones. Even then, I did not covet an excess of possessions, but I was pleased with his gift to me, not a book this time but an engraving of my Lord in a silver frame. I can see it now, as it sits on my side table. I cherish it still.

As the sky darkened and the night drew in, I could see that my father, the mighty and merrie John Mann, was quite subdued. He was making a great fuss of the little one, Dottie, showing her the carved, wooden doll he had brought her. He held her tight upon his knee as he made the doll dance about, in the flickering light of the fire, while looking intently at her sweet face as she laughed. However, after the others had retired to bed, and with a mug of ale to fortify him, my father, almost shamefully, confessed to me that he had visited the Bedlam. The hospital had recently moved to a new site at Moorfields and was receiving much attention. My father said he was curious to examine the new accommodation, which surely had to be an improvement on the old hospital, built hundreds of years before, and he had agreed to accompany some wealthy men he was about to do business with. As he sat and slowly recalled his visit, his mood became even darker until he growled, 'New buildings perhaps, Mary, but nothing new in the care of the poor wretches under its roofes.' He sighed, and then explained his discontent: in the new building, long galleries had been constructed so that visitors could better observe the lunaticks. Even worse, many of the rich and powerful people of London regarded the inmates of the Bedlam as entertainment, or as a show even, and they visited only in order to have something to laugh about at their supper parties. But, though my father could entertain with the best of men, he was horrified by this inhumane and disgusting abuse of those poor tormented souls. He was with men he respected, and whom he had traded with for years. So he was astonished to see his companions laughing at those poor wretches who were in so much distress, goaded by the warden, who banged the doors of their cells to inflame them further and who encouraged the visitors to prod them with their walking canes. It seems the warden was paid a few pence for this show. My father was incredulous; he could understand that the rich have often acquired more money than sense, though that gave them no excuse in his eyes. But he couldn't fathom why there were also poorer visitors wasting their pennies on this cruelty, money that should have been put to better use, to feed their children and improve their own lives. Though my father tried to reason with his companions, they could not see why he was so disgusted, and I am forever proud that my father turned his back and walked away. He refused any further dealings with them for many years, though it did not seem to harm his business.

For want of conversation, one day, I repeated my father's account of his visit to the Bedlam to my eldest sister. She was newly married, to Talbot Pepys, a distant relation of the renowned Member of Parliament Samuel Pepys. Through our family connection we had heard about the exploits of this Samuel Pepys, a man much given to entertainment and, it seemed, a trial to his poor wife, due to his attraction to many of the women of his acquaintance. My sister then told me, boasting a little, of a visit her husband Talbot had made, an outing to the Bedlam, organised by his famous relative for two visiting girls, supposedly for the purpose of seeing how mad people truly behaved, after a visit to the theatre, where madness had been acted out:

EXCERPT FROM THE DIARY OF SAMUEL PEPYS

18th February.

Up, and to the Office, and at noon home, expecting to have this day seen Bab. and Betty Pepys here, but they come not; and so, after dinner my wife and I to the Duke of York's house, to a play, and there saw 'The Mad Lover', which do not please me so well as it used to do, only Betterton's part still pleases me. But here who should we have come to us but Bab. and Betty and Talbot, the first play they were yet at; and going to see us, and hearing by my boy, whom I sent to them, that we were here, they come to us hither, and happened all of us to sit by my cozen Turner, and we carried them home first, and then took Bab. and Betty to our house, where they lay and supped, and were pretty merry, and very fine with their new clothes, and good comely girls they are enough, and very glad I am of their being with us, though I would very well have been contented to have been without the charge. So, they to bed and we to bed.

19th February.

All the afternoon I at the Office, while the young people went to see Bedlam, and at night home to them and to supper, and pretty merry, only troubled with a great cold at this time, and my eyes very bad ever since Monday night last that the light of the candles spoiled me.

I was disappointed to hear that the 'great' Samuel Pepys, renowned and admired, seemed to have condoned a visit to the Bedlam, that most cruel entertainment. Though sadly he was not alone, as apparently many in London saw it as quite an acceptable pastime. I would have rather more respect for this man, and others in positions of influence, were they to talk of kindness and charity rather than glorify the torment of those poor unfortunates; they could do so much to set a good example and change attitudes. Even now, I sometimes despair. Truly I do. It takes so little of oneself to be kind.

FOR WANT OF A CARRIAGE

I heard another sorry tale, this time of a lord (no less) who had his wife admitted to the Bedlam. It appeared that soon after the birth of his fourth child, she had shown signs of worsening hysteria (that most female of complaints, or so it is claimed). He could certainly have afforded decent care for her, but he was rather keen to remove her from his house, and, it seemed to me, to remove himself from any responsibility towards her. He never visited her, not once in more than three years and, rich though he was, he stopped paying the regular sum that would at least have eased her time there. She was lodged with the other inmates, the poorest, and suffered who knows what torments. It was also said that she was hidden away when the rich and loathsome visitors came for their entertainment, for fear that she might be recognised. She cried constantly for his presence, and even shouted out that she was a lady, the wife of that prominent and most important lord, but tragically her claim was put down to her lunacy. And, of course, rather conveniently, the more she protested, the madder she was deemed to be. There were those who knew the truth. But this lord was a man of great importance, who had such control over other people's lives that no one would speak out against him for the damage he could do to them. He installed a new woman in his wife's place, similar looking, I'm told, but unlikely to disgrace him with any emotional outbursts. And the great and the rich of London society accepted her and pretended that all was well, for no one dared to challenge him over his neglect and cruelty.

I was young then, but I wish I had been courageous enough to name this lord, and though I was sorely tempted to shame him, it would have caused trouble for the person who told me that sorry tale, so I remained silent. I wished, too, that I could have taken a carriage to collect that poor woman and move her to a place of safety, of kindness, far away from her tormentors, where she might have received treatment and had a chance to recover, but in those days I did not know of such a place, anywhere in our kingdom. Even so, I could not help but feel ashamed that I did not have the strength of character to walk to the marketplace and hire a carriage to take me to London and rescue her. I thought of the writer Aphra Benn, a braver woman than I, who had quite a reputation for encouraging women to speak out, but though I read her words over and over, and though I could form all the arguments in my head, somehow I could never voice them out loud. Meek and mild still, I did not even tell my sister that I disapproved of her husband's visit to the Bedlam.

Four

'MY MOST BELOVED, SAMUEL'

The years passed and I continued to do my duty to my kindred. My thirty-third birthday came and went. I was still unmarried. I was told that I was plain and at my age not likely to find a husband. I was a devout servant of God and I accepted His will. Still, sometimes I wondered, what of another life? As a daughter of the richest man in Norwich, the daughter of a mayor of Norwich, indeed, why should I not have been courted, desired? Why was there not a queue of suitors for me, as there had been for my sisters? So, in the absence of a husband, I had to ask, was I truly that plain? My sisters said I had too much goodness inside me, and though it may have sounded like they said it kindly, I could tell they regarded it as a bad thing. That it put men off. I did not know if that was true. Though I was sure I did not wish to be considered desirable by the flatulent, fleshy oafs that visited our home to court favour with my father.

And so I remained the thoughtful, helpful, devout daughter in the family, assigned to the care of the sick and the tormented, the unmarried daughter who served God by caring for others. That was my life and I accepted it. I remained ignorant of love and those aspects of marriage that my sisters blushed about. Though I was relieved that I did not have to suffer whatever trials some women, on occasion, remained darkly silent about.

I had a reputation for kindness and was considered a most gentle nurse for the sick of mind and body. I decided this must be God's design for my life. I would serve Him, I would do good, and I would offer what comfort I could. But, I had to wonder, was this God's whole purpose for my life? Was this all? Was it enough?

The poets talked of love. I loved my father, and dear Ellen, and of course I loved my mother. I loved God. But I knew there was a different kind of love, a love I had not experienced, though secretly I imagined it, read of it, in pamphlets I kept hidden:

How strongly does my passion flow… I languish, sigh, and die.

Indeed. This was a love I longed for but feared I may never know. A passion I could almost feel, a restless fever, a desire never quite in reach. And though I certainly did not languish for I was far too busy, I did sigh. But I kept those thoughts to myself. After all, to those around me I was 'unmarried Mary', 'sensible Mary', and who would suspect that I had such longings beneath my pious exterior? Still, it was best not to dwell. I counted my blessings. I reminded myself that I was able to remain in the care and protection of my father. We lived in an agreeable house in a safe part of Norwich, and we had good food, warmth and companionship. I looked around and I could see many who were much less blessed than I. And I was wholly grateful that I did not suffer the distress and torments of the mind that I could see in some of my family and in people wandering our streets. I would open my Bible and read. The good words filled me with joy and hope, and I was thankful for my life.

And yet… And yet…

One day, I rather reluctantly accompanied my father to a service at the church of Thorpe-next-Norwich, situated to the east of the city, and he insisted I meet the new rector there. I had heard he was a most pleasant, pious man, and a friend of my father's, but then my father had a lot of friends, and I was expecting some dusty old cleric. I was not prepared to come face-to-face with that lovely man from all those years ago, the man who had held my hair in my dreams more times than he would be comfortable with. Samuel

Chapman, now the Reverend Chapman, no less. He was older; we both were, though I might still have been a young girl for the effect he had upon me. We were introduced, and, though he was polite, he did not acknowledge that we had met before.

At the end of the service I looked for him, but he was surrounded by a twittering flock of his parishioners, all keen for his attention. I had no option but to return home with my father, evidently looking rather flushed, as he rather pointedly commented. I brushed aside his intrusion on my thoughts, although of course I was aware of the heat that filled my whole body, and all the way home I could barely contain my desire to see this man again.

The days passed, and, though I was already a most diligent and regular worshipper at our usual church, God must have been exceptionally pleased for I started to attend services at Thorpe-next-Norwich too, under the pretence of accompanying a great-aunt who was a parishioner there. During the service, standing before him, I, the pious Mary Mann, barely moved my lips, nor sang my praises to God, as I watched him. I confess, I loved to watch this man. I noticed the way he moved, assured, as if he always knew exactly where he was going, but moving more slowly, more gently, around the little children and his frailer followers. I noticed his hair, resting on his shoulders, and dropping over his eyes as he lowered his head to read the lesson, and his mouth as he formed the words. And I started to think how it might feel to gently place my hands on his face, to move his hair away from his eyes. But I kept these thoughts to myself, I confided in no one for, in truth, there was no one who would listen and, really, I had no desire to share him.

He was a popular man, always surrounded by others who appeared to need his blessing more than I. And though I had taken to rinsing my hair with water infused with rosemary, I could never get close enough for him to notice. Finally, after four interminable Sundays, on a wondrous, sunny day, I had the chance to speak to him again. Before the service, and in the presence of my father, he simply looked at me and asked if I could spend some time with his poor wife, who was mortally ill. Of course, I agreed. My father had already given his permission and as we all stood and talked, as I stood close to this man, I noticed that his beard was showing traces of grey along his jaw, and I had to force myself to move my eyes away, to be able to concentrate on what he was saying. We continued to engage in our public, polite exchange, and, then, incapable of caring if I was observed, I looked at him again and I noticed his eyes. Those knowing eyes, with their shadows and traces of dark melancholy. I knew that, like us, he had family who had suffered the torments of madness, and parishioners who had been afflicted and whom he, and God, had been unable to truly help.

Annoyingly, our conversation was interrupted by the approach of one of his needy church women loudly claiming his attention, though, before he turned to her, he caught my eye and gave me a fleeting smile, then a slight grimace. I felt a rush of joy as we shared that moment, an understanding of how we must both fulfil the roles we had assumed, to be always patient, polite, respectable, but that, like me, he had another side to him, one that he was rarely allowed to show to others. And so I saw beyond his loveliness and I had a glimpse of his loneliness. I delighted in the look he gave only to me, but, as I moved slowly, reluctantly away, I had the strongest feeling that he could crumble at the lightest touch, the softest breath, at the sadness of all that he had seen and all that he knew.

LOVE ALTERS NOT

Night after night I dreamt of him. Every afternoon, I visited Margery, his wife. I felt she welcomed the distraction I provided, but I noticed that she looked constantly for him. I behaved perfectly in their presence; I was kind, devout, caring Mary Mann, and a credit to my father.

The very worst side of me emerged, as I noticed with a horrible glee that she was not looking so good, her hair was dried and dull, though she still had a fondness for lace, and a frail sort of prettiness, while I, I had to admit, did not possess any sort of prettiness at all. I was dreadful. That poor woman – what on earth had she done to deserve my cruel thoughts? She loved that man, that's all, the man I loved with all my being. Still, I resolved to be kinder, and I prayed, asking God for forgiveness for my mean spiritedness. I made an effort to distract Margery from her illness, but she refused to engage in conversation, and insisted instead that I read the sonnets of Shakespeare, over and over, as if to show me how much she loved her husband, as if to prove that their love would endure:

Love's not Time's fool, though rosy lips and cheeks
Within his bending sickle's compass come:
Love alters not with his brief hours and weeks,
But bears it out even to the edge of doom.

So jealous was I of their union, that those words of love became vile in my mouth, a vicious bile. Margery seemed not to notice and often fell into a kind of trance as I read. Well, as if another's words of love were enough, as if words were going to save her. I observed, with unkind pleasure, that he left the room as I read, that he, too, disliked those sickly sonnets. And I knew, also, that he preferred the great Bunyan, and his *Pilgrim's Progress*. The afternoons passed too slowly, but I was content that my visits occupied her and allowed him time to sit in his study, writing his sermons, or so he said. But I was certain that he didn't work in there; he simply sat, surrounded by all his books, looking out of the window. I had the feeling he brightened when I entered with a dish of tea, which he had not requested but that I had decided he would like, all the same. And then as he turned to me, I was filled with joy as we talked politely about nothing at all, for all the while I was aware that his gentle eyes were resting on my face.

The days passed. And each day I hoped that I would see him, but most often I stomped home, cross that he was elsewhere in the rectory during my visit. And then, one beautiful afternoon, he sat and listened as I read to Margery, those sickly-sweet words. I was forced to pause, unable any longer to speak such words of love, out loud, in his presence. Believing I was finished, he stood to leave, and, for want of something to distract me, I draped a soft shawl around his wife's shoulders, and he, Samuel, looking long at my hands, commented on my elegant fingers. That's what he called them. Elegant. Then he blushed. And turned away.

Despite my excitement at this brief show of feeling, I soon became distraught when we returned to our distant, polite, very formal interaction when I went to sit with Margery. A nod. An acknowledgement. Then he moved away, unable to meet my eyes. Some days I did not even catch sight of him. Though I admit I desired to. I admit I desired much more. This madness of love took over me, and I, the good and devout Mary Mann, at the mercy of my longing for him, even considered taking him a tonic made with Solomon's Seal, for I had read that it was used by some as a love potion. Fortunately, I was able to restrain myself and I realised that I must stop my ungodly thoughts. I tried to remind myself that he was married and that he was devoted to his wife. Of course he was. It was devastatingly apparent to me in the tender way he attended to her, and every day I suffered more to see him behave so.

I resigned myself to my unremarkable life once again. Family. God. Caring for others. Placating the lunaticks. Not unhappily, but not happily either.

Years before, I had been described as 'a most pious and faithful servant of God' by one of my sisters' laughing suitors. He certainly did not mean it as a compliment. Thankfully, maybe, I hope, even loyally, my sister rejected him. I was reminded of his comment one afternoon as I was leaving the rectory. I overheard two visiting clergymen describing Samuel in exactly the same terms. They were clearly stating their approval. That he was a 'most pious and faithful servant of God'. Could it be that my sisters were right, that I had too much goodness in me? But could it possibly be, could I hope, that, far from frightening Samuel away, it was what drew him to me?

I looked again, more closely, for signs that Samuel thought of me, too. But, as if to punish me for my thoughts, my father received a short message from him to say that I was not required at the rectory, that I no longer needed to attend his wife. And so, I stayed away. Still, though, I was able to watch him in church. How he moved, how he talked. It seemed he did not think of me at all. If anything, he had become cold towards me, even avoiding me, and then I could see how little he laughed, and that he was just mouthing the words to hymns, not singing with gusto and joy like before. But then I understood. I heard of the mortal illness that had afflicted Margery's mother, like many others in our city, and though I knew of Margery's own ill health, I assumed she had simply moved home to care for her mother in her final hours. Then I heard that, just three days after her mother's demise, Margery also succumbed, and that Samuel was in mourning at the loss of his wife. The mother and the daughter. They were buried in the little churchyard in Thorpe where Samuel was minister, and the words I had to presume were in his heart were inscribed onto a stone in the rear of the chancel of the church.

MARGERY, THE DEARLY BELOVED, MOST PIOUS
AND MOST FAITHFUL WIFE OF SAMUEL CHAPMAN,
MINISTER OF GOD'S HOLY WORD TO THIS TOWNE

'Dearly beloved'… of course she was. And those words stabbed at my heart. So I kept away, and I started caring for another poor distracted parishioner, then another, and another. I took consolation in my love for God and though my feelings for Samuel remained strong, I made sure that I behaved well when I was unable to avoid him at church. And time passed. Slowly. But it passed.

And then everything changed.

Two years after Margery's death, when smallpox had once again taken hold of our city and had already carried off an abundance of people, I made one of my regular visits, to an elderly parish clerk who was slowly and peacefully dying (though of old age, not of smallpox), and Samuel was there. We spent two hours, in a gloom barely lit by spluttering rushlights, talking soothingly and sharing God's words with the dying man, until eventually, with a sigh, he passed, seemingly pleased to go. As we left, just at the door, Samuel paused; he gently took my hand and softly kissed my fingers.

And yes, much to my father's delight, Samuel asked for my hand in marriage. And yes, we were the two happiest people on earth. And I knew I was not plain, that I was loved, that I was the 'dearly beloved' one. And I came to know, with delight, what my sisters blushed about and that there was nothing in my marriage I need ever remain silent about. And yes, I knew fierce passion, as our bodies, and our souls, were entwined. And I thanked Him for finding Samuel. And I heard Samuel praying and thanking Him for finding me.

We were married in May, at the great church of St Peter Mancroft in Norwich, close to my family home and where my father usually worshipped. My father ordered new garments for everyone, and, though I was not given to colourful clothes and adornments, I was persuaded by my sisters to put cornflowers in my hair. I insisted, too, that I leave my hair long (that shocked them a little), loosely plaited and twisted to the side so that it flowed over my shoulder. I wore a dress sewn by my father's own tailors. The skirt was kept plain in cream brocade, with a pale gold front panel. And the bodice, oh, my delight at seeing the intricately embroidered flowers – all the ones my father knew I loved – the roses and columbine, cornflowers and honeysuckle, all surrounded by vines and little bees, and spangles that caught the light. I looked closely at all the detail and shed a few happy tears as my eye was drawn to a tiny canary in gold thread amongst the vines. I was quite overcome with joy, for I had thought I would simply wear my best day dress, that I would make do. With the promise of new clothes for themselves, my sisters had secretly taken one of my dresses to ensure the correct fit and I could see my father's pride when I reacted to his gift with delight. Knowing that I preferred to dress plainly, they told me they had thought I might be cross and refuse to wear it. How little they knew of my love for Samuel. For him, I would be the most beautiful I could be on that most beautiful of days.

And, as much as I usually shied away from being the centre of attention, I was so happy that day, surrounded by my family, and free at last to show to all, to show to God, my love for Samuel. I only had to glance at him to know that even in the midst of all those people he, too, had eyes only for me. We exchanged rings, gold bands inscribed inside with words that only we could read: 'Our two loves become one'.

After the marriage service, we travelled in a great procession, reflecting my father's status, to my new home, the rectory at Thorpe-next-Norwich. The celebrations began, though in truth I wanted only to be alone with Samuel. Later, just as my father decided to break into song, I took myself away from the merriment for a moment and stood at a distance, hidden under the swirling embrace of a willow tree, to remember my darling mother. I wished with all my heart that she, who had worried about me ever accepting anyone at all to marry, let alone a man such as Samuel, could know that I was so content. In her final days she was angry about dying before she could see all her children into adulthood. All she wished was to know that we would be all right, that life would be kind, or even when life was cruel that we would not be alone, we would have someone by our side, to help us through. And I, who had actually breathed a sigh of relief when I met Samuel, wanted to pull him to her, to show her, to say, 'Look, I have found him, you can know that I am content, and you can rest now…'

At peace, I decided to return to the rectory, and as I gently moved the fronds of the willow tree aside I saw Samuel striding towards me. As we met he folded his arms around me and I sank into his safe embrace, where I intended to stay, for all time.

I moved my few belongings into the rectory at Thorpe-next-Norwich and started my life with Samuel, my great, gracious man. I noticed, rather wryly, that I had gained much status as a married woman, the wife of the Reverend Samuel Chapman. I was no longer the 'poor spinster', the plain Miss Mary Ann Mann. As the rector's wife I was treated with even more respect than I had received when part of my father's household. And, given that Samuel had served the parish church for many years, and was much admired by the local women, who had a keen eye for a lonely widower, I was surprised and a little thankful that even his faithful parishioners accepted my presence in his life.

Ellen had moved in with us, for I could not contemplate leaving her behind. She chose the large room downstairs where I had nursed Margery, and immediately occupied herself, quite determinedly, by moving all Margery's possessions out (which suited me) and her own things in. Once she was settled, Ellen was quite calm for some time, appearing tired and sleeping a lot but not excessively sad. She spent her days dusting, sorting and re-sorting all Samuel's books in his study, quietly ignoring him. And, though I sometimes saw her sitting and turning the pages of one of his books, I doubt that she took in any of the words, for she seemed quite lost in her own world.

I had insisted that I preferred the upstairs room at the side of the rectory, the one overlooking the garden, which we made into our private sleeping room. Coincidentally, of course, this was a room that held no memories for Samuel of his first wife. And we used the smaller downstairs room as our main living room, though we spent most of our time in the kitchen, which I gradually made my own, filling the shelves with my pickles and preserves, and moving Margery's things out of the way, into a cupboard at first, and then finally out of the house, to be distributed amongst the needy.

And the walled garden that stood between the rectory and our church, well, that was truly mine, for Margery had shown no interest in it, and I cleared and planted it with vigour. Samuel had understood my passion for he turned up one day with some half-dead roots, declaring them to be a newly discovered, and highly sought-after species of rose. He had looked so pleased with himself and I planted them with care, though I was not convinced they would survive. The next summer we were rewarded as they bloomed almost overnight and filled our garden with loveliness – a memory that still fills me with hope. He also presented me with a copy of *The Elements of Botany*, by that most renowned apothecary Hugh Rose. I read it every night by candlelight and kept it near me in the kitchen, absorbing all the knowledge there, brushing out old pastry crumbs that must have become lodged in its pages when he carried it back from the bookseller. So, if I came across some remaining possession of Margery's that had been missed, well, I felt no jealousy, for I was with him now. And the rectory became our home, which we filled with our own memories and, of course, with our own precious love.

My life was transformed into a churchly routine. As the rector's wife I was in great demand. With my visits to our poor parishioners in need of care, whilst still looking after Ellen and visiting my father, as well as running the household for Samuel, I was stunned with exhaustion most evenings. But the prospect of seeing Samuel walking up our path at the end of each day, then the door closing firmly behind him and the world outside shut away, to sit at our table for supper, with the evening ahead, just us two, was perfect, perfect joy. And each night, finding that my dreams were realised, those dreams that had sustained me for so long. His hands, my hair, and, joyously, knowing what came next.

We were in the full flood of our happiness, a few months married, when a comet appeared over the summer skies. We stood together by the graveyard of our little church and watched as this wonder tore across the sky, showering all the living, the lost and the dead with its great light. We stood for a while and reflected on those loved ones who had left us, and this great love we had found. We were disturbed a little, though, by the raucous singing coming from the White Lion Inn, near to our church, as it rang out, '… and… she wed him, she fed him, she bed him, she…' then Sam gently put his hands over my ears so that I should not be shocked by the words of those popular rounds, which were becoming louder and smuttier as more ale was consumed. Laughing, I pushed him away and we chased each other back towards our happy little home, through the gate and along the path. Then a sort of madness of happiness infected us, and to the tunes coming from the inn we danced uproariously around the garden, falling about, giggling and clinging on to one another. We were only half-aware of passers-by seeing us, being protected by the tangled branches of the willows that seemed to dance along with us. Later, I wondered what they must have thought, seeing the upstanding, learned rector and his calm, respectable wife behaving like crazy people. Oh well. Finally, we could dance no longer, and radiant and exhausted we sank onto the cool grass and lay side by side, sharing the glow of the bright-lit sky, our long, elegant fingers touching.

Later that year, as winter approached, we attended the funeral of the physician, scientist and writer Sir Thomas Browne, who had died exactly seventy-seven years to the day of his birth. It was held at the church of St Peter Mancroft, and it was my first important appearance, amongst the great and the good of Norwich, as the Reverend Samuel Chapman's wife. I couldn't resist wearing my new dress, a rich, green taffeta, brought back by my father from the Royal Exchange in London, though I covered it with my plain black cloak for the sake of propriety. I held my head high as I watched others watching others and I made sure to stand close to Samuel, my hand lightly resting on his arm, so there could be no doubt who I was and that he was spoken for. And, though I truly do not like such occasions, I played my part. Then finally, having exhausted all my empty, polite conversation, I was relieved when it was time to go. Of course I was happiest as we strolled away, just the two of us, alone, together, Samuel listening patiently as I chattered on, yet again, about Thomas Browne's radical thoughts and his *Religio Medici*, his 'pure flame… and invisible sun' glowing within us.

Our joy continued. In the Long Frost that came the following year, the River Yare froze over and we skated together. I was reluctant at first, concerned that the ice would not hold, but Samuel held me tight and pulled me gently towards the edge of the crowd of skaters on the ice, who were all shrieking with delight. In my mind, Samuel and I joined hands and we flew around, graceful and oblivious to all. But in reality, of course, we slipped and slid around the stalls that had set themselves up along the river to take advantage of the trade. But he held me up, and we smiled, though we were quite frozen, unaware that our red-faced joy was obvious to all. And it is true – that love keeps you warm.

In those long winter months, it was freezing, even inside the rectory. We closed most of the rooms and heated only Ellen's room, our bedchamber and the kitchen. We were more fortunate than most for we could afford wood for the fires, though it was in short supply as the forests had not yet recovered from the decimation of the Civil Wars. Samuel took wood to those of his parishioners who were most in need, and he helped to plug gaps and draughts in their walls with rags and clumps of straw where he could. Ellen and I baked bread and made a great pot of pottage from our store of roots and vegetables from our garden. We kept it going for many weeks with regular donations of offcuts of meat that my father had managed to procure from somewhere. Samuel spread the word about his parish that the poorest and those in genuine need could call in as they passed the church, and we also took bowls of this pottage snug in boxes of straw for those who could not leave their dwellings. Sadly, we could not feed everyone for there had been a pitiful harvest the summer before and food was already scarce, but at least the poor and miserable could look forward to one hot meal each day.

Before the fire in our room died down each night, we wrapped ourselves in layer upon layer of our warmest garments until we could barely move in bed for the number of coverings that we had upon us. I could hardly see Samuel for all the nightcaps piled upon his head, though I could see his beard and I could find his lips, and that, for a time, had to suffice. And as much as I usually loved to inhale his earthy scent, especially in that deep hollow in his neck, as I traced down from his lips, I had to admit that even he had become a little pungent. As, possibly, had I, for I had noticed that he was keeping his distance. He had used all his favourite rosemary-infused soap and had to resort to the soap I had scented with oil from our own roses, though for once Samuel did not laugh or complain that his hands smelt like those of a girl. I had strewn rosemary and bay all about the rectory, and I continually sprinkled our garments with rosemary water, but it had little effect for we were unable to wash and dry our underclothes as often as usual, and all round it was not a pleasant time. After three long months, we gave thanks to God for the thaw. It was a delight to shed the weight of those layers and be able to move with freedom once more when we unwrapped ourselves. And not only us, for on the first fine day the bushes all around and about were hung with clothes drying in the spring sunshine, as we and our grubby neighbours emerged from our hibernation and our grime.

In the world outside our little womb of happiness, a king died and a new king was proclaimed. Parliament, as ever, continued to argue. Religious differences still disrupted the peace, and wars were fought. Norwich itself was fairly calm, though we heard of discontent elsewhere. We lived through it all, for the most part untouched by the troubles, and content in our own little corner of the world, secure and together. The days, weeks and years passed, and we were happy. Of course, at times we could both sulk for England, and our petty squabbles often lasted for days, neither one of us wanting to be the first to apologise, no matter how great our love for the other. I did wonder if he ever despaired of marrying me, for, at least when alone with him, I was now not afraid to speak out, to voice my opinions, as I had found someone who seemed to delight in my chattering. I was my father's daughter, after all, and I made up for all those lost, silent years when my thoughts did not seem to matter. Sometimes when we argued I would just hold out until finally, defeated but laughing, Samuel would give in and admit that I was right. And then I tried to be gracious. Of course, I did take notice of him and I did realise that he had a much quieter way than me of pressing home his opinion if he knew himself to be correct. And, if he truly believed he was right, he would not budge. And then I would think over his words, and, though it might take me a few days to see the sense in them, I would show him that I understood. Perhaps during supper, I would airily and in a roundabout way let him know that I had listened and considered, and that I truly valued his opinion and I regretted my sharp words, though I could rarely bring myself to say sorry. And he would nod, and carry on eating his supper, and supping his ale, and, with a half-smile, he would accept what he knew to be my apology. And in this way we strengthened our bond.

In the early years of our marriage, when we were still getting used to each other, we once had an argument that had festered for some days, over the rights and wrongs of the outcome of the Monmouth Rebellion. Samuel, tired of war and futile death, was advocating a peaceful solution, and I was for people doing their duty, whatever the cost. We could not reach common ground, each of us coming up with new reasons to support our opinion and both of us unwilling to listen to the other, or to let it go. Our usual calm contentment was disturbed, and I began to doubt. I started to compare our loving but lively relationship with that of others. I had seen the quiet, compliant little wives at church, always deferring to their husbands, and I began to wonder if Samuel might have been better off with one of those. Did he perhaps want just a wife and not an equal? Did he marry me out of loneliness? Did he regret choosing me as his wife? Our disagreement deteriorated as I became uncertain, fearful of losing his affections, and then I became spiteful. I festered for a while, unwilling to forget our quarrel and meet him halfway, even though he made several attempts to make peace with me. Finally, exasperated, he simply stated, very quietly, 'I love only you, I want only you,' and he refused to argue with me any longer, though, I am now ashamed to say, I continued to goad him.

One evening, exhausted by the loss of our togetherness and wanting to get away, I left the rectory and sat under our willow tree, watching the amber glow of the sky as it faded and cooled. I felt my mind come to rest, and remembered how feisty my mother had been, able to stand up to my father even though he was a most dominating person and used to having his own way. My mother would never accept the quiet life if it meant conceding to him when he was wrong, at the expense of her own self. And I could see that my father had been a better person when he was with her, that she also made him who he was. I remembered that my father had appeared reduced after her death, shattered by the loss of her, and for a time he was quieter, as if uncertain of himself and of his purpose in the world. Like Samuel and me, they had chosen each other. My mother had rejected many of the potential husbands selected by her family and had firmly refused to marry at all until she met my father, and even then she had insisted that he wait until she was quite sure. And Samuel had chosen me. He knew I was different to Margery and that he would not have an easy time, but still he had chosen me. I looked down at my hands, my still-elegant fingers, and saw my wedding band as it caught the last glints of the sun, and I remembered how Samuel had insisted that he too would wear one, as a sign to all that we were tied in the same way. He was unusual in his beliefs and was teased for this by some of the men in the parish. Most did not believe in equality, and, though their wives wore a ring, that gold band represented ownership by their husband. Such a belief was abhorrent to Samuel. And I knew that. And I was ashamed that I had ever doubted him. I rose and hurried back to our little house, feeling the warmth seep from the stone walls of his church as I passed by. I could see Samuel through the open door, sitting at our kitchen table. He had left the door ajar to make sure I was safe, knowing I was outside alone, as the night descended. He knew me. He had left me to my own thoughts, knowing I would not want him to chase after me, but he had made sure he could hear if I needed him or called out. Distraught at my silliness, and for risking the love of this man, I went straight to him, before he could rise, and I put my arms around his shoulders and kissed his silvered hair, and I apologised. I said I was sorry, this time spoken out loud, and I told him how much I loved him, how he was my heart, my world. And I resolved to tread more softly.

As I hurried along the path to the church the next morning I recalled that cold, cold winter, the year after we were married. I had been bustling around our cosy kitchen, preparing our evening meal, and singing loudly, happily, the most joyous hymns I knew, and expecting Samuel to hear me and burst through the door and join in. Three hymns later, though, and pausing for breath, I realised that he had still not returned. He had been outside for some time to clear the snow from the paths around the church, but he should have returned by now; the sky was dark, and the air was growing heavy and icy. I went to the door and called out to him, but only silence replied, my words, like my breath, fading into the night. Concerned and fearing he had suffered an accident, I grabbed my cloak, hitched up my skirt to keep it dry, and, moving cautiously on the freezing path, I went to find him. In the gloom by the edge of the graveyard I could see his shape on the ground, on his knees, moving the snow frantically. He saw me, looked up into my face, his own a ghostly grey and he held up his hand. Not realising what he was trying to say, I reached for him, but he pulled away, and finally I could make out his words. He had been shovelling the snow, trying to keep warm… he had removed his sodden gloves from his shrunken fingers… his wedding band must have slipped off… he had only realised it was missing when he had started to come inside. And he had been searching ever since for that little gold band, in the frost and the gloom. The sky had turned black, and, with no lantern or moonlight to help us, we could only slip slowly back towards the rectory, still scanning the ground as if by some miracle the ring would appear. At the door we both turned to look at all the paths snaking around the graveyard, covered by the wintered branches of the shrubs and hedges, and silently we realised how futile our search might be.

Back inside, in the warm, Samuel sat by the fire, oblivious to his poor cold hands, itching and sore, turning from skeleton white to flamed red. I knelt by him, offering words of comfort that he met with a guilty stare. I tried again. After all, it was only a lost ring, and I had feared so much worse when he hadn't returned. We still had what that gold band represented: we still had each other. I took off my ring and pressed it into his still-cold hand, and made him read out loud the inscription: 'Our two loves become one…' 'We still have that,' I told him. 'Nothing could ever take that away.'

He looked up at me and spoke slowly, softly, words from our favourite book: 'I wonder, by my troth, what thou and I did, till we loved?' I held out my hand and he gently placed the band back on my long, elegant finger. I kissed him and returned my attention to our abandoned supper, humming my hymns of hope and joy.

It was one of the longest periods of the coldest of weather I have ever experienced, in that bleakest of times, as the snow laid solid on the ground for three full weeks, defiantly resisting

Samuel's desperate digging. At last the snow turned grey and slid away and, though the frost lingered, he was out there again. Still looking. But we were unable to find that little glittering band. I expect it is there still, waiting only for us. I sometimes saw him, as he ambled his way to his church, stop and bend down and move aside the wild flowers that grew alongside our paths. Or, when he was talking to one of our more demanding parishioners, I could see the toe of his boot poke out and surreptitiously move the grass at his feet, still hoping to find it even after all that time. I imagine our circle of gold sinking lower, with each passing winter, still with the warmth of his finger upon it. I hope that, as we could not find it, no one else will, that it will remain hidden forever, a remnant of our love, and after our bodies are buried and decayed, and our gravestones are grown over with moss, it will reunite with us once again in the deep earth.

GLORIOUS, BLOODLESS, REVOLUTION

Our country had a revolution. It was glorious, or so we were told, but at least this time it was bloodless, and our rulers changed again. King James II decided to leave his throne and his country, and he was succeeded by King William and Queen Mary. At last, in my lifetime, we had a woman on the throne, but, though they were said to rule jointly, it appears it was not to be equally, for the real power was with William himself. Why was I surprised? Little of importance really changes.

Though the world around us moved on, our world stayed very much the same. We had our routine. The day-to-day of waking together, discovering every morning anew the delight of not waking alone, then separating to become our public selves, the rector and his wife. Later, returning home to our shared meals and our contented evenings, reading to each other from our books, our wedding gifts to each other, then to our prayers, and our shared nights. After Samuel had drifted off to sleep, I sometimes looked back to the younger me, to my fears of dying a dried-out old maid, my fears of missing out on such joy, such pure undiminishing pleasure. I wanted to throw open the window and lean out, and, with my nightclothes wrapped loosely around me and my hair long and messy from Samuel's caressing hands, to shout into the night, 'What a wondrous God. This is all with God's blessing.' One such night, in the midst of a terrible storm, and as if to show me His might, I saw, out of the window, flames in the sky, towards the sea. I tried to rouse Samuel, but he was snoring for England and I let him be. In the morning he smiled, kindly, but a little disbelievingly, at my description of the fire in the sky, yet when he returned, later that day, he admitted he had heard of the church in Yarmouth where a bolt of lightning had struck the top of the spire, causing a fire that had taken many hours to be drenched. So perhaps what I saw was not a sign directly from God that He approved of our passion, but I believed He approved nonetheless.

Several years into our marriage, I had noticed from time to time that Samuel had been getting more tired than usual, but I was not too worried, as we were busy, he was always in demand and he would always recover his vigour. We had chattered our way through another winter, but he was hit by a particularly nasty chill, during the Great Gale of 1692, when we were out and about for many nights and days aiding our parishioners; Samuel helping with repairs and rebuilding whilst I provided care and tonics for those who had suffered because of that ungodly weather. Much of Norfolk was devastated, though most of the damage was to buildings that could be repaired, and thankfully there was little loss of life. One poor gentleman, though, hurrying home along the river after the worst of the storm had abated, was knocked flat out by a piece of timber blown from a roof. Samuel was called to attend to him, but he arrived too late – the man lay on the ground, stone dead.

Despite this awful tragedy on our own doorstep, we felt we had perhaps escaped the worst of that tempest, but then we heard of the terrible tragic night when around 200 sail of ships and more than 1,000 people had perished in the waters off Cromer. With our own loved ones safe, we prayed with, and for, some of the families of those thousand dead. We asked that God had granted their loved ones a peaceful death, though even with my faith, I found it hard to truly believe, for we had all seen, and could not forget, the violence of that storm.

When the repairs were complete, Samuel was finally persuaded to rest, having taken cold. I nursed him with tender care, insisting that he slowly sup a warming lemon posset when all else hurt his throat, and eventually he began to recover. Soon after the storm, when we felt that the world had returned to normal, Samuel and I had taken some bread and cheese, and a bottle of the ale I brewed, to sit in the warm shadows under the willow by the river and watch the wherries from Yarmouth, with their black sails and white noses, carrying their herring to the annual fish fair in Norwich. It was a bright and clear afternoon and we were sitting close, sharing our simple meal, and smiling and feeling… well, just joyful. Without warning we were disturbed in our happiness by a great shuddering of the earth and for a few seconds we were quite terrified, believing perhaps that this moment was the world's last. We looked around to see if others had noticed it too but, save for a few geese that had taken flight from the river, people merely paused. Before long the bustle of the river returned as the rivermen resumed their shouting and jesting, and the geese resettled on the uneasy swell of the water. We supped the remainder of our ale and returned home to our chores, and by supper-time, still complete in our happiness, we had forgotten all about our earlier fright by the river.

We were disturbed once again, though, this time by a great banging on our door, which was opened by Samuel with some consternation, only to find my father in quite a state. Fearing that the great shudder had been caused by an explosion like that of the Great Blowe, he had travelled across Norwich to visit each of his loved ones. My father was quite perturbed and implored us to pack some necessities into a small trunk, ready to move to the safety of his house should the city be under attack. We managed to calm him and promised to prepare to leave, though we declined to go with him, reasoning that we were safer away from the city for we were by the river and had a ready means of escape should we need it. All remained peaceful that night, and we began to wonder if we had imagined it; indeed, a few people we spoke to from outside the city had failed to notice any disturbance at all.

The next day we called on my father, who had just returned from the Angel, where travellers on the stage coaches were reporting that an earthquake had been felt all over London, the severity of which increased the more they quenched their thirst. My father, usually a coldly decisive man in business matters, was a little embarrassed that he had reacted in such an uncharacteristic manner and apologised for causing us to panic (though, in truth, it was only he who had panicked). I loved that even in his advanced years my father's first reaction had not been to guard his home or his trappings of wealth but to protect his family, all of us now adults and with our own to defend us. I loved that, having raised and protected us for so long, he was unable, like my mother, to truly let us go. I could see he was getting older, still a forceful man, a presence, but I was struck by the sad thought that one day we would have to make our own way without him beside us. But for now, we were all together, all secure, all content.

I CAN ONLY BELIEVE IN GOODNESS

A few weeks after the earthquake, on one of his visits to the gaol in Norwich, Samuel was asked to say prayers with a prisoner and he attended regularly and dutifully, as he always did, though he rarely explained the circumstances of his visits. Then, one dreadful day, he rose before dawn, washed his face and hands, and dressed, searching crossly for his whitest, newest collar and cuffs. Dark and silent, he picked up his Bible and left the rectory. I could barely make him out but at the little wooden gate he stopped and looked back at the church and seemed on the verge of turning back but then, head down, he marched towards Norwich, and his shadow soon disappeared behind our weeping willow. I was waiting when he returned, much later, but he went directly to the church and prayed for four straight hours, not moving. I checked on him from the doorway but felt compelled to leave him be, his great black bulk emanating all kinds of dark distress. Later, in the cold silence of the night, as we lay next to each other in the warm pool of our bed, he opened his eyes and talked. To me? To himself? Well, he had already talked to God, and at some length, and for once it seems that God had not answered. But at least I could show him that I was listening, and slowly the truth of his day emerged. He had been required to attend a prisoner, a soldier, to hear his last words and to bear witness to his execution. That soldier had been shot for desertion, in the Chapel-Field that morning. Poor Samuel was distraught; though a peaceable man, he had raged, furious that the army leaders, with no regard for guilt or innocence, could stoop to such a barbaric act. Those men had ordered the deliberate death of one of our own soldiers, who was but an exhausted boy; tired of trying to act like a man, the man he would now never be, he simply went home to his mother, to a place of familiar people, to love. For that error, that boy had been executed. He had already fought, in the line infantry, the bravest of soldiers, and indeed, his captain had described him to Samuel as one of the most courageous of his regiment. But nevertheless, it had been decided that in order to maintain discipline, the poor boy's life had to be sacrificed, if only to set an example to others.

It was so unlike Samuel to vent any fury. For as long as I had known him, he would always carefully consider each side of an argument and then quietly state his case, but on this, well, he could see no reason or justification whatsoever. He managed to carry on his duties for a few more days, but he was always to be found in the church until late, praying for that poor departed soul. One moonless night, when he had still not come to bed, I walked down to the church and waited and listened under the embattled tower, but, hearing only silence, I moved into the nave of the church. Finding him prone on the unforgiving deadly cold of the stone floor, with great effort I managed to raise him to his feet. Holding his hand tightly for fear he would fall, I walked beside him, slowly, back to the rectory, and all the while silent tears were falling treacherously down his face.

In the warmth of our kitchen, he withdrew the boy's sad possessions from his pocket and lined them up on the table. A hair comb, a small pack of playing cards, a spoon worn thin, and a clay pipe – his tobacco pouch already taken by another prisoner. Finally, a small, tatty book of popular ballads, picked up on his travels – for his mother, who had a sweet voice, he had told Samuel in his last hours. Samuel climbed the stairs, slowly and deliberately, and lay down, still clothed. I wrapped the poor boy's things in a cloth and left them on the dresser. And I went to lay beside my Sam.

The next morning, he was still awake, though I must have dozed. I went to prepare a tisane and to warm some bread, but when I returned he had not moved, and, unusually for Samuel, he remained in bed. Claiming he had taken cold, I asked the rector of the neighbouring parish to cover Samuel's services and I discouraged all visitors to the rectory, standing in the doorway, if needed, to block their attempts to push past me. And Samuel slept and slept. During the day, at those times when I would not be missed from my duties in the parish, I went to lay beside him, to console him. The shadows in his eyes that I had seen when we first met had returned, and as I lay, waiting for him to wake, I vowed and prayed to God that I could soothe them away once again.

When he woke, he would turn over towards me, and in the light from the afternoon sun, with tears still falling, he would lightly touch my face, his own full of the knowledge of the true evils of men. And I held him, and I resolved to give him time, for it was all I could do. I was heartened that he would at least respond to me, even if he couldn't bring himself to talk. Gradually the anger in him that had turned to sadness turned back to anger and the tears stopped. Over the next few weeks those dark dreaded days faded, and he slowly returned to himself, although not completely; he was forever changed, forever saddened.

If we were two joined as one before the death of that poor boy, then afterwards Samuel seemed to breathe my own breath. He was constantly looking for me, needing to be near me, to be reassured and safe. He would move his books and papers into the kitchen if I was there, content to work for as long as I was nearby. He looked for me in church, his eyes on me, deep into me, while he read the words of God.

I was happy to be so close to him but one day, in our garden, I joked that whenever I turned around he was always under my feet, and, a little impatient, I fetched a shovel and pointed him towards the road to collect some of the horse dung that filled our streets, for our precious new roses. He smiled as he took the shovel from me, and then he spoke, 'But, Mary, I can only believe in goodness if you are near.' And I made no more comments – I just let him be. And so, I might be busy, pruning and harvesting, and turn to find he had moved to sit on the wall to read, close to me, but just far enough away not to irritate, and he would look up and grin, happy that I was checking where he was, knowing that I needed his presence too. We had always laughed a lot, talked for hours, spent nights not knowing where one of us ended and the other began, but, looking back, perhaps those quiet days together were our most blessed times.

For a few years, there was the usual turmoil in London, and from Scotland rumours came of a dreadful massacre at Glencoe, but, for us, time passed peaceably enough, though we were not without our losses. My two elder sisters died, yet I did not mourn them greatly. They had not been particularly friendly to me as we were growing up, and the memory of 'Meek and mild, Mary Mann…' still stung, more perhaps because they had been right: I seemed unable to bear a child. But they had been excited for me on my wedding day, and the Lord teaches us to forgive, so I forgave them their unkind words. I noted their passing with regret, but that was all.

My father was more affected by their passing than I had expected, and he became quite sentimental, again using my pet name, Mary Canary, and talking at length of my mother, and our childhood, telling tales that I had mostly heard many times over but a few that were new. For a while he became quite sprightly, demanding that Dorothy should accompany him to various old haunts of his. They went to the New Hall, where he would sit contentedly for a while surrounded by all those familiar books. And he insisted that he visit the Angel Inn to warm himself with their brandy, though he tired quickly now of the debates and disagreements of the men who had succeeded him and were the new rich and powerful of Norwich. Of course, Dorothy refused to enter and left him there whilst she found sanctuary in the nearby drapers' shops. As dusk descended, my father would return, exhausted but with a soft smile on his face and, deep in his thoughts, he would sit and stare into the fire, then doze peacefully, long into the evening.

At Kensington Palace, on the twenty-eighth day of December 1694, Queen Mary died, aged thirty-two, of the smallpox. We read that the king was grief-stricken at her death, even saying that he 'had done with the world'. As a consequence of another cold winter, the queen's funeral was on 5th March, when the great bell of every parish throughout all England was tolled for three separate hours, from nine in the morning to ten, from two to three, and from five to six in the evening. My father was irritated by the clamour of the bells, which he said left his ears ringing so much that he had been unable to find any peace all day. I was told by Dorothy that he was certainly very vocal in his complaints, and she had to admonish him regularly as he uttered his favourite phrase, 'kiss my arse', to anyone who had the misfortune to pass by. Sadly, I was not to be one of those who heard his last thoughts, even his angry ones, for the very next morning my beloved father was found dead, still sitting in his chair by the fire. I was quite unprepared. He had appeared well in the weeks before his death and there had been no sign that this was coming. I regret, of course, believing that we still had time, that I had not taken the trouble to sit with him, to remind him of my love, and to thank him for all his care, for all of us, for all of his life.

I often wonder if he had any time, as death approached, to look back, to think of us, to say a silent goodbye. I wonder if he remembered that day at the Angel with the elephants. Though perhaps I should wish that he didn't suffer the torment of knowing that he was leaving us. I hope and pray that he passed peacefully and unknowing. Perhaps it was just his time. He had had a long life, a life well lived, and he knew he was loved. I pray that was enough.

MY FATHER'S DAUGHTER

Samuel was by my side as we buried my father at St Andrew's church, close to my old childhood home. Many of the rich and powerful men of Norwich, the great and the good, attended, and most were anxious to tell me how well they had known him, particularly in his later years, when he was important and 'the richest man in Norwich'. I was a little curious about their claims as I had certainly never laid eyes on some of them. I retaliated, as a counter to their banal talk of wealth, with details of all the bequests he had left in his will, and of the 100/- he had designated to be lent out to four weavers, for five years, interest-free. Yes, he had been rich, but he also wanted to help others, to give them a chance, to maybe make their own fortunes, to help them care for their loved ones. Above all, to make their own way in life, as he had.

Then a man who was neither great nor good, an occasional acquaintance of my father's, came up to me to offer his condolences, but as he spoke his respectable words he let his eyes travel over my body and linger, despite my mourning dress and obvious discomfort. I did not know how to tell him I did not welcome his attention, aware only that it felt quite unlike the times when Samuel rested his gaze upon me. Flustered and angry, but seemingly powerless still, I fell back, as I always did, on my dignity, and I simply moved away, hiding amongst the other mourners. Finding Samuel, I tried to explain why I was so upset, but he took my distress to be caused by the sadness of the occasion and bent towards me to gently wipe away my tears with his thumb. Yet again, I fell silent. After all, it was just a look, wasn't it? And I was married to Samuel, so what harm could that man possibly do to me?

My father's closest friends were also present – all were conspicuous in their care of me, the older ones even stating that they had promised my father they would look out for me, and support me, and that they would keep their word, I had only to ask… I was a little taken aback by their assurances for they were saying more than the usual words of condolence, but later, piecing together several conversations, I think I understood. My father must have confided in them that he believed I would achieve something great in my lifetime. He knew he had been lucky to survive for so long, for almost nine decades, but now he had entrusted these men to act for him, to protect my interests if he did not live to help me himself. I was curious about what he thought I would do. I was forty-six years old and I had lived an unremarkable, though blessed, life. What could I do, in my remaining time on earth? Indeed, for the first thirty-five years of my life I had simply resigned myself to doing good deeds, to doing my duty, with only the occasional thought for my own desires. But I realised, too, how my life had changed when I met Samuel, how I had discovered true passion and the greatest of loves. So yes, perhaps there was still time. I was my father's daughter, after all.

MY GREAT, GRACIOUS MAN

We had not heard much news from London since my father's death. In truth, we let the decisions of the king and the men in Parliament pass us by. Most were of no concern to our lives and we were content to live in our little rectory, close to the parishioners we tried to serve well, and whom we had grown so fond of. We paid little attention, then, when Parliament passed legislation to regulate our silver coins, which had been clipped and filed and reduced so much that they had all but lost their value. The old coinage was being collected in and new mints were erected at various towns and cities about the country. Norwich had one mill and one press and began to produce the new coins in September 1697.

A month later Samuel was taken ill again. It had begun to rain on 4th October and continued without a break or any sign of the sun until noon on the tenth day of that month. The rain caused such a rage of waters that it overflowed the lower part of the city and it did so much damage that it washed away the city bridges.

We saw men rowing their boats along the streets, for it was the quickest way to travel, and I was reminded of my father, telling his tale of the Great Flood of '46 that had reached into the very centre of the city. That immense weight of water had caused much distress as it moved relentlessly through the streets, filling homes with its stinking mess and destroying precious possessions. My father chuckled a little as he went on to tell of the young boys of the city who were able to cause havoc and row freely along streets and alleys now empty of horses, traders and bossy adults – and how they had called out to each other with delight as they claimed the streets as their own. Most of them made a good few pennies by ferrying people around and transporting goods to those in need. They provided a cheerful though rather costly service, as they were able to name their price. My father loved to tell this tale for he had quite admired their enterprise, and their eye for making money, a desire close to his own heart. But he also respected their tenacity, their desire to make some good come out of difficult times. As ever, he ended his story by quoting the Mann family motto, *Per ardua stabilis,* 'strength in adversity', a belief by which he had lived, and which had served him well. Strength in adversity – a phrase I would often have cause to repeat to myself, as I met with my own challenges, in the years to come.

However, in this, the latest in a line of difficult times, we were certainly standing firm. My dear kind-hearted Sam was out once again, mending, helping, repairing, and he suffered a chill so violent that he was confined to bed for three whole weeks. He had grimly laughed, as he coughed, at the richness of so much silver hoarded at the Mint whilst he and the poor of Norwich fought, with few resources, to repair their pathetic abodes. The money that could have helped them, that could certainly have saved some lives, was locked away. Samuel was quite bitter, and raged a little, in a fever, of the distance between rich and poor, how it had always been so and how he did not have faith that it would ever change.

With rest and good food and my own hot tonic of meadowsweet, he recovered, but he was struck down again the following year, after being caught in a snowstorm in May, as we endured another bleak and seemingly endless winter. It took him yet longer to recuperate this time, with a cough that persisted. I kept him supplied with tonics and syrups and even forced him to drink an infusion of 'Heal All', and, though he got no worse, he got no better either. But he struggled into his great overcoat, which hung loose about him now, and trudged into his church before he was quite recovered, to reassure his faithful parishioners that he was fit and well, though I doubt they were fooled for he was much thinner and weakened in body. In spirit, though, he was immense. His vitality, his determination to live every moment infected us all. His sermons shamed the richer men of the parish to donate to those in need – wood for repairs, blankets, bread – whatever they could spare. Even the church ladies, who usually spent more time talking of their good deeds than carrying them out, were urged into action, and our older parishioners received more soothing possets than their toothless mouths could cope with.

For the next years we were busy, almost mad with desire, united with an undeterred passion, to make life better for others. Filled with renewed vigour, Samuel made repairs to the rectory, dug and weeded alongside me in the garden, planted trees, repaired the wall and cleared the path. He even brushed all the moss from the gravestones in our little churchyard, so that the names of the dead could be brought back to life once more. He visited again and again all the lost and the lonely. He arranged day trips: we rowed along the river, strolled as the sun set, and watched as the sun rose over our pretty walled garden. He produced small gifts, little surprises, a handful of cornflowers, a sweet cake, an embroidered frog purse, all to make me smile, to make me happy. And I did smile, and I was happy. Joyously happy. And Samuel? My beloved Samuel. He wouldn't let go. He wouldn't rest. He held me, loved for all time, in his safe embrace.

Five

'IT WAS MUCH UPON MY GOOD HUSBAND'S THOUGHTS'

I will pause now, as I look back at my life, for I have come to the part that troubles me still, even decades later, for the details are burnt upon my heart. Perhaps I should tell of that day as though I were there once again. Imagine me, then, newly dressed in my widow's black:

It is the second day of July 1700 and my beloved Sam is dead. My most gracious and faithful Samuel is dead, and I am bereft at my loss. He has gone, and I cannot follow…

It pleased Almighty God to call my beloved husband from me just three days and three nights ago, and I have been exceedingly troubled. I have begun to fear that I might, like my mother in her last years, sink into the deepest darkest melancholy, for I have lost my most precious Samuel, whom I entirely loved and who made me all that I am.

But for now, I have gathered my senses, and today I have buried my husband, my very heart and the kindest of men, in the chancel within the church of Thorpe St Andrew, where he was minister. I am comforted to know that he was so well regarded that he has been buried inside his church, not in the little graveyard outside. I stood and watched as they lowered him into the ground and his grave was filled, throwing the roses I had cut that morning down to him with each shovelful of the soft earth from the floor of his church, refusing to move until his coffin was completely covered.

And I stood and listened as people told me of his generosity. That he had left money in his will for a school master to teach six of the poorest children of the parish to read. That he bequeathed money to his old college, Corpus Christi in Cambridge, for the maintenance of scholars in need. And that due to his generosity we will all benefit from a sermon on Plough Monday each year. I know, too, of the eleven shillings he left to the poor in bread and cakes. All this I already know. All this we discussed. And I do not need to hear any more talk of his kindness, or his grace, for I have breathed in his words, his soul, for all these years, and I have him within me for all time.

Today, this most desolate of days, I have shaken so many hands and listened to so many well-meaning but seemingly endless words of sympathy with as much dignity as I can manage. I am a calm woman, controlled, polite, everyone says so, but, truly, I want to scream out at my loss. My loss. For who else can understand that great love I shared with my great, gracious man.

I see an opportunity, and, leaving the other mourners behind, I start to walk away from the church. At last, I can allow a few tears to fall, but, as I wipe them away, I look up to see the man whose eyes lingered on me at my father's funeral step into my path, blocking my way. He is bold now, in the absence of both my father and Samuel, and this time he takes my hand in his, soft and repulsive, and he leans in close to whisper that he is willing to take me on, that I should be his wife, when my period of mourning is over. I catch the rank odour of his unwashed clothes, and I pull my hand away – it slips from his with ease – and I stutter out a muddled 'Sir, but… Sir, you… misjudge me', then I push past him and hurry down the path, through the little wooden gate and away.

I walk far along the river, until I forget that most unpleasant encounter. For now, I have left Sam, and our home, and our little parish church, behind me; finally, and thankfully, I am alone, with my grief. I watch the wherrymen and their boats, with their catch of herring, and I find strange consolation in the knowledge that the poor of Norwich will have full bellies for a few days at least.

I pass under the great willow where Samuel and I used to sit, and I can feel its boughs drooping low around me, as though it knows that even the tincture I made from its bark could not save him. I remember our times by the river, under that immense willow, as it cloaked us and held us together, and I start to look back at my life with Samuel. Astonishingly, I am able to smile. I praise God that He has seen fit to grant me the most contented eighteen years I should ever have imagined. I shall keep my memories of Sam, his strength, his deep laughter and, above all, his faith in me and his love of our life together. So, with my heart filled with love and the certainty that I will one day be reunited with Samuel, and in the love of God, I take comfort that his funeral was so well attended by his many faithful parishioners, whom he cared for with such generosity.

I had also noticed, between my tears, that my father's rich and influential associates had once again made an appearance. Well, let the powerful show their power; they do me no harm.

Calm once again, I continue further along the riverbank, briskly now, and I plan the inscription on Samuel's gravestone, which shall be of black marble and shall plainly read:

SAMUEL CHAPMAN, AN HUMBLE ADMIRER OF YE GRACE AND WISDOM OF GOD IN A CRUCIFIED JESUS, FELL ASLEEP IN THAT JESUS, THE HOPE OF GLORY, THE RESURRECTION AND THE LIFE, JUNE THE 29TH, 1700

I am content with these simple words, for my memory of him is sufficient to sustain me. There will be no showy memorial, for I know he would not have approved. My memory alone will give him life, as it does to all those we have loved and lost, each and every time we remember them.

As I walk, I reflect on those precious years I shared with Samuel, our evenings together, peaceably reading our books by firelight, our strolls through the streets to visit our parishioners in need of care or kind words, and our hours spent together in our little walled garden. My pace slows as I rediscover our grief, long buried, of not being blessed with children of our own, children who would have been so loved. Though we had tried to accept their absence as being by the grace of God, we still questioned, and we prayed, looking for an answer. And I am struck by a new sadness, remembering our desperation, and the pain that came with each new moon. I remember when Dorothy asked me if I had my pleasure with Samuel, if it was my lack of joy in our union that hindered a pregnancy. And, summoning all of my Christian patience, I was able to calmly reassure her that if it was simply a matter of my pleasure, if that was all that was required to produce a child, as many believed, then I would be a mother a hundred times over. She giggled at that, a rare event. And even I managed a smile. 'Yes, we take our pleasure according to the old-fashion,' I could not resist adding, 'And also the new fashion,' which made her shriek with laughter, then blush at the thought of the serious and sensible Mary Chapman being so adventurous, while I, too, flushed as I recalled sitting astride my husband. But though our sorrow at our want of a family increased as each year passed, thankfully the subject was gently dropped. And even my father, who produced children as easily as winking, saw no reason to condemn me for the lack of another grandchild. His only comment, once after church when I was bluntly being asked by one of the pushy church women why I was not yet pregnant, was to say loudly and clearly, 'My Mary has much to achieve in her lifetime. You wait and see.' And that settled that. I was thankful that neither Samuel nor my family saw my inability to bear children as an affliction. And I was thankful, too, as I offered up my prayers to God each night, that I had been free to choose Samuel, the best of men, as my husband, and he to choose me.

We talked these many long years, Sam and me, as we cuddled, warm and safe, after our first sleep. Not wanting to waste a candle, we lay in the darkness as our words spilled out, words that did not come so easily in the daylight, between the Reverend Samuel Chapman and his pious wife. But at night, we shared a language that we both understood, and we told of ourselves and our lives before we met. Our fears, our losses, our joys. We talked, too, of politics, of war, and of the happenings in our little world around and about the parish. Of the horrors we saw, the struggles of the poor, families devastated by the effects of the plague, parents destroyed by the loss of a child, and, of course, the loneliness of those without a child to survive them. I know how it weighed upon him, as he gave prayers for the little ones, so many of them, here at Thorpe. But I know, too, that he took comfort that their names at least were carefully recorded, by his hand, in our parish register, as reminders of this cruel life, to be read in the centuries to come.

We spent many nights talking of that which was closest to both our hearts, the suffering we had seen amongst our own loved ones, afflicted with the pain of mental torment. We were both united in our condemnation of the barbaric bleeding and pointless purging advised by our medical men. We had seen for ourselves how these treatments had so little effect, and we had begun to read of a new type of doctor, who believed there could be a physical cause for a loss of the senses, that not all suffering might be explained by a simple imbalance of the humours. Samuel and I tried to acquaint ourselves with the advances being made in science and medicine, and we both had hope that a cure might be found for the many disorders of the mind. We made time to talk to the older parishioners, about their primitive beliefs, to attempt to persuade them that it wasn't God who cast these afflictions upon the deranged, that lunaticks were not being punished by God, that they didn't 'deserve' to suffer so. Sam and I were in agreement about this, as in so much else. As we talked, we planned;

we looked for ways we could help to alleviate the most grievous mental distress, not only for the relief of the afflicted but also for their kin who agonised to see them suffer so.

I look up and I see a wealthy couple, with their rich clothes and their satisfied smiles, strolling towards me. The man carries a silver-topped cane and I am reminded of a night, many years ago now, when my father repeated his story of his visit to the Bedlam, that dreadful place, and how Samuel had sat and listened with revulsion, then anger. I recall my father's horror and disgust at people's treatment of the lunaticks there, where they were goaded for the entertainment of those who were free from such torments, a place where it was even deemed acceptable that men could bang their canes on the bars of the cells to inflame the worst of the lunaticks, to make them 'perform'. I also remember, as clear as if it were yesterday, that, once our anger and indignation had worn away, we had reflected that perhaps those people, the tormentors, had no direct experience of caring for loved ones who were so affected. Samuel had suggested, in his quiet way, that perhaps we needed to consider setting a better example so that people would be less in fear of lunaticks and thus able to show them more kindness. And he was right, of course. My beloved Samuel.

I march on, wanting to be away from that couple who seem to flaunt their wealth and good fortune, appearing to be free from any cares. As they pass they try to catch my eye, to wish me well, or maybe, seeing my mourning clothes, to acknowledge my loss, but for once, not caring how I am perceived, I turn away, strong and bold. I hear them mutter at my rudeness and I want to confront them, for can they not see my evident distress, my wild hair and pale eyes. I want them to act with compassion, to understand my loss, to let me be, for today at least. Thankfully, the moment passes as I find the strength to ignore them and soon they are gone.

I become aware that I am the only woman without a companion, and that there is no longer another half of me striding alongside, and I feel very much alone again. I hurry back along the riverbank until I can see the reed thatch of the roof of our church through the trees and only then do I slow to catch my breath. Other mourners notice as I approach, and I am surrounded before I have even made it back through the gate. I am now grateful for the attentions of these people, for their presence at least stops me being alone for a while longer – delaying the time when I will have to face my loss all over again. This endless day. But the great and the rich do finally leave, content that they have been seen to have shown their respects in the proper manner. Those who truly wish me well hug me for a final time as they gently take their leave.

As I try to summon one last bit of strength to say goodbye to my family, I step into the tranquillity of the church for a few moments, and I see a tiny woman dressed in black, standing in the shadows next to Samuel's newly covered grave. I march up to this person, wanting her to be gone, but, as my eyes become accustomed to the gloom, I see that she is holding a tiny posy of wild dog-roses, her hand shaking. She looks up at me, her eyes faded and wet and her body trembling. She reaches into the pocket of her frock, for a handkerchief, I presume, but instead she pulls out a tatty piece of paper and pushes it towards me. I feel a cold creep through my body as I recognise Samuel's handwriting. 'My boy…' the woman says, but that is all she can manage, and she sags, faltering. I guide her gently towards the pews so that we can sit, and we spend time together, just there, near Samuel. She looks down at the little flowers, now resting, wilted, in her lap. Plucked from a hedgerow as she walked here, for she is poor, I can see that. But they are tied with a bright white ribbon, bought new, it seems. I take them, gently inhale their scent and lay them on his grave, above his heart. She nods at me then takes a breath and stutters out her story, though I already understand. Her son, her boy, the soldier shot at the Chapel-Field, with Samuel by his side in his last moments. She looks up to the light shining through the windows of the church and recites, without hesitation, the words in Samuel's letter. She pauses. Then, 'He brought me peace,' she says. She stands, and places her hand on my shoulder, then silently leaves the church. I sit. And I sit. Clutching that letter. The letter written by Samuel to explain an unnecessary death. The letter he had taken in person to that distraught, disgraced mother, with a note from the boy written in Samuel's hand but told with the boy's words, and his few, final possessions.

My memory wanders on for I remember how Sam had returned to me that night, angry and sad once more – but my thoughts are interrupted when, with a crash, the church door is pushed open and the sexton hurries in, looking for me. It seems my brothers had become concerned that they could find no trace of me, fearing I had disappeared towards the river once again, but I am irritated to be torn away from this memory of Samuel and I huff out a breath. Still, I rise and, with my voice shaking but my words firm, I instruct the sexton to inform my brothers that they must grant me a few moments alone with my husband. I stand by Samuel's grave and see the bare earth beside him. I recall that in his last hours, in between his feverish mutterings, he had told me he had made arrangements with the bishop for the space beside him to be kept empty until God chose to take me, too. And how his eyes had filled with tears as he said, 'Mary, fight them if you need to, but we must stay together,' – then a half-smile – 'decay together.' I had agreed, of course, and a representative of the bishop, today, has reassured me that it will be so. With this thought, I walk out of the church and somehow I find I have the fortitude to say my final thank yous and God-be-with-yous. I am comforted at last, on this dark day, by that poor woman and her memory of my gracious husband. I realise, then, that I should have sent for a carriage to take her home, but she is gone.

That evening, looking for some peace, I reassure my family that I am indeed in control of my senses and that I will see them the very next day. They fuss around me, of course, but I insist, and they leave, a little thankful, I believe, to have done with me and my misery, for that night at least. Inside, I close the door, take a breath and I look around. I can see Sam's great heavy long coat, still hanging by the door. It needs brushing for it is coated with dirt from the last time he wore it, but I do not have the energy. I see his chair by the fire, the cushion still shaped by his body. I can see, all about the room, his gloves and papers and tools, all strewn around, where he left them. His hat, left hanging from the door handle, catches my eye, and then I see our books, our gifts to each other, bought on our trips to Norwich from the bookseller by the Guild Hall. I stand, in the mess, for I had not thought to tidy this room, our room, in those long days after his death.

He had been laid, in his woollen shroud, in his coffin, in his study, where the walls had been draped with black crepe. I had sat by his side, straight and deathly calm, while the mourners, summoned by the solemn bells of his church, brought their sprigs of rosemary and rue. And now I go back to that room, sickened by the smell of the spices they used to mask his body's decay, and I firmly close the door. I decide that I will ask one of the many people who offered their help today to come and pack away his books, for I will not enter that room again.

OUR TWO BLOODS MINGLED BE

I return to our kitchen and look around at the remnants of his untidy ways. If he had a fault, and of course he had many, though that did not stop me from loving him for an instant, it was that he was quite a messy man, and at times it drove me to distraction. I would try to arrange his possessions, to make order, so that he would be able to find everything when he needed to, but he would soon muddle my system. I smile. He once quietly and patiently commented, as I busily returned his mug to the dresser, not noticing that he had only just reached it down to pour himself some ale, that he sometimes felt like a little bit of an irritant, like one of the fleas I worked so hard to get rid of. And, quoting John

Donne's poem, which we knew so well, he pulled me towards him. 'Mary' – his eyes glittering as he looked upon me – 'this flea is you and I…' and, laughing, I placed my hands on his face and replied, '… with one blood made of two…' and then, together, '… our two bloods mingled be…' No, he was not a flea, but he was, on occasion, my clumsy, messy, rumbling irritant. My wonderful, wonderful irritant, whom I will love for all time.

Surrounded now by all his untidiness, the mess that he will never return to move or misplace again, I stand a while. Stunned. I realise that I am alone in our house not only for tonight; I will be alone for the remainder of my life on this earth. I cannot even hope that my beloved Samuel will stride through the door and comfort me. Can that really be true? That I am truly alone? He is nearby, I know, but I resist the urge to walk over to the church to where he is buried – the thought of seeing that dark-turned ground and knowing he is there would be too much to bear. All I can think of is how cold it must be deep underground, but I know that cannot trouble him now. I go to the door to lock out the night, and I wrap my arms around his coat and hug it tight, inhaling wood smoke and rosemary. Curious, I push my hands into the pocket of his coat, hoping to find some little piece of him that he had left behind. I find some of the stalks of rosemary that he chewed to clean his teeth and a piece of pastry crust from the last pie he bought, perhaps only a week ago, from the stalls along the river path back from Norwich. Those pies that he loved and thought I didn't know about, though I found the crumbs often enough. In another pocket I find a linen handkerchief, the one, and there was only one, that I had struggled to embroider in the early years of our marriage, when I was trying to be that sort of good wife. It is still folded, and the stitches are still uneven. I put it back and, though I continue to search, there is no love note to me. Had I really expected to find one? No, of course not, for I know that he did not expect to die, and I already know that he loved me. I look around the room again and decide to leave all his mess just as it is – it may be of comfort to me again in the morning.

I light the fire in our bedroom, wrap myself in his nightshirt and hold his nightcap close to my face, inhaling all that is left of him, finding solace in the softness of the linen. For now, his scent, so dear to me for so long, will have to sustain me. I am unable to sleep, and in truth I have no desire to; I simply lie there, holding on to his memory, not wanting to start another day without him. I have lost count of how many times I have been told by people who are trying to console me that I must get on with my life, perhaps even remarry. That time will heal. How little they know of love; how little they understand our love. I pick up my volume of John Donne's *Songs and Sonnets*, a present from Samuel after the first year of our marriage – the pages I have turned and the contents I have absorbed. I hug my book close. I know I will never again read Donne for fear my heart will shatter, but I open it and read Samuel's inscription, in his untidy hand:

> *If our two loves be one, or, thou and I*
> *Love so alike, that none do slacken, none can die.*

As I lie, I can see my hair upon the pillow; it has faded, dulled, the life gone from it and there are already more shadows of grey in the days since his passing. I wish to tear it out, knowing that he will never again hold it in his hands, or hold any part of me. We had lain here one night, newly married, talking of our great fortune in finding one another, and I couldn't resist asking him if he remembered our first meeting, at my father's house, in that bleak year without summer. A year I remember with warmth for it had brought me my first sight of Samuel. 'Of course,' he laughed, 'how could I not recall a woman who was quoting Thomas Browne's *Urne Burial*?'

I persisted, 'Then why didn't you seem to remember me when we met at your church?'

'But Mary,' he said, remembering it all, 'you were so fierce that day at your father's, you looked so angry and I had only just met you. I couldn't work out what I had done wrong, or how I had offended you.'

To me, happy now, it was obvious. 'You hadn't married me,' I retorted.

And he pulled me to him. 'Oh, Mary, my love, my life. I wish it had been possible. But we have now. We have everything. We have this.' And I argued no more.

BELIEVE ME

Crushed once again by this sweet memory, I watch as the warm glow of the embers fade away. Samuel's letter is in my pocket, returned by that poor boy's mother. It is pressing against me and I pull it out and move towards the window to read it by the moonlight. That silver light, the one thing we still share, for I can see that it is shining through the windows of his church and down over his grave. I look towards the church tower and I remember Samuel coming home from his visit to that mother, furious that she had been shunned by her neighbours, and even by the rector at her parish church, for being the mother of a deserter. How she had been abandoned by her husband who had been unable to live with the shame. Samuel had recounted that, when he visited her, she had taken her son's letter containing his last words, held it for a moment, then placed it in a little wooden box on the mantle, to remain unread. Then she had asked Samuel to read his own letter, for there was no one else she could ask. He read it, he told me, over and over, as she sat:

Mistress Blackthorn,

I am sending you a letter from your son, who asks that you remember him kindly. We sat together, and I wrote down his words for him, so they are true. Also, a little book that he wanted you to have. I am grieved to have to tell you that the sentence of death was carried out today. I feel very upset about him as he was such a nice boy, and a braver man than I. I am glad he did not suffer much at the last, for, after sending his love to his father and mother and all at home, he walked out with such courage to face his end. I can tell you that he died quickly, for I was there. I trust you will find comfort in this for he has given his life for his country quite as much as if he had died on the battlefield. And he seemed at peace. Believe me.

Yours,

Samuel Chapman

Again, I sob.

And I remember Samuel's words to me years before, trying to console me when, after another moon had passed and I was still not with child, I had been tempted to rage at God. Sam had recalled his visit to that boy's poor mother and described again her anguish, her unbearable pain at her only child's death, 'Mary, it is God's way and at least He has spared us such a loss.' But I turned on him then for I could not see the sense in his words. I could feel only my loss of those unborn children, our own little Samuel and Mary. When my fury had passed, I went to sit by him and I held his face in my hands, and I could see the pain in his eyes, the pain he had hidden as he tried to console me. Now, for want of a child of my own who might support me at this time, now that he whom I loved with all my being has left me alone, I am angry again at his quiet acceptance. And I cry, like never before, for all of my losses, throughout all of my life.

That endless night.

I must have dozed for when I wake I turn to the side of the bed where Samuel used to spread his great bulk and I reach out my hand to stroke where his face had rested, every night of our eighteen years together. The bed is hard, and I can feel each one of the lumps for he is no longer here to shake out the mattress. He used to laugh as he pounded and punched to soften it for me after I had complained of another uncomfortable night. I determine to forget my anger and think of him with joy, for that is how we had spent our lives together, little pockets of pure joy in amongst years of contentment. The moonlight moves on and darkness soon fills the room. My mind wanders to other times spent with Samuel and I flit between memories, trying to remember them all, not wanting to lose one precious moment. But, tired out and perhaps prompted by my meeting with the man with the silver-tipped cane and his wife, I cannot stop myself thinking of those horrific stories coming from London's Bedlam, and my heart fills with a futile sorrow for those poor people there – a worse place to be incarcerated I cannot imagine. Even now, in the midst of this uncontrollable dark grief at the loss of my beloved, I know that I have the support of my family and the love of kind friends, and that with God's grace I will recover.

Words from an evening spent with my father keep forcing themselves into my head, and our conversation about that dreadful prison for the mad, the Bedlam, will not leave me. How Samuel had questioned my father about his visit, wanting to know all. What did he see that was good? What type of lunatick was held there? Were any people ever released, or cured? Were the medical men who treated the poor unfortunates deliberately cruel or simply baffled, unsure of what to do to help? Endless questions as Samuel tried to order his thoughts, to make his plans. We had heard, soon after that conversation with my father, of the death of a generous man, William Doughty, who had left £6,000 in his will to his trustees to build a hospital for the poor men and women in Norwich. We had talked for days of this man's desire to do good for those less fortunate than himself, and it had prompted Samuel to leave a bequest in his own will for the support of Doughty's Hospital. I ponder, and at last my mind is able to rest. For it was much upon my good husband's thoughts to also contribute something towards the perpetual maintenance of such a place, not for the poor and destitute but instead for such persons as are deprived of their reason and understanding, a place for those who are without relations or friends to take care of them. With this realisation I am filled with a strength and determination that I will find a way to create a monument to my love for Samuel, to build a hospital where even the poorest lunaticks will receive kind and caring treatment – a place where they will not be tormented or abandoned. In Samuel's memory, this hospital will stand and reflect the kindness of his soul, the goodness of his very person.

BETHEL, HOUSE OF GOD

I remember, also, when Samuel, full of his hopes and plans for our hospital, had woken one night, not long before his sudden decline, and pulled me close as he whispered, a little feverishly, in my ear, the name he had chosen, 'Mary… Mary… it should be called *Bethel, House of God…*' I had been somewhat irritated at being woken and had pushed him away, but now, I realise, the name is perfect, and I am determined this is what our hospital shall be called. I also notice, a little grimly, that the name Bethel appears on first sight to be similar to Bedlam, but by the grace of God how different I intend them to be. If history can indeed call back time, I am determined that our Bethel shall stand as a true testament to hope, even if people only remember the Bedlam with fear and disgust. The Bedlam and our Bethel must not be confused when history records my efforts. I will set out such clear instructions for the management of the Bethel; indeed, I will live there so that I will be able to oversee all the lunaticks and their care for myself. I will ensure we worship our Lord regularly, so that we may all gain comfort from His words, and perhaps we may also persuade others to look upon the lunaticks as God's people, people whom He has not deserted: unfortunates perhaps, but people still, in need of our understanding and our care. So maybe, with God's grace, the shadow that has threatened to darken my soul since He chose to take my beloved Samuel from me may not linger. I know I cannot follow him until God chooses to take me, but it is possible I will not fall to the devastation I now feel. Perhaps I will be able to survive this.

Later I wake. Cold. The fire has died down, but I cannot bear to stoke it up again as I can remember all the times Samuel and I had sat in front of its glow, wrapped up together in our big blanket while we held our clothes in front of its warmth before dressing, shivering and laughing. But there is no more warmth, there is no more Samuel. As I lie in the darkness, at the end of that dreadful day, I am forced to consider: what else do I have left?

In my life I have had three passions, my beloved Samuel, my faith in God, and a desire to do good for the poor lunaticks of this city. My love for Samuel will endure, and, for now, I am able to hold on to my faith and I pray that will be enough to see me through. Then I remember my father's words, often repeated, *Per ardua stabilis*, 'strength in adversity'. Though I am more tired than I could ever have imagined, I will pray, and I will hope, I will stand firm, and I resolve to continue a little longer.

I lie for a while, and then, feeling the chill of a new day as the dawn breaks, I drag myself out of bed, to begin again…

It was 1700 and I was fifty-five years old. A woman, alone. But I would endeavour to build the House Samuel envisioned, a hospital for the care of poor lunaticks, where they would be treated with kindness and the hope of a cure. It was such a task, one that I would have to achieve without my Sam by my side, but it was clear what God had intended for my life. I had my faith in His purpose for me and my strength from my love of my darling husband. I had the name of the hospital at least, the Bethel, the House of God. This was Samuel's vision. I would build his House. Of that I was determined.

Six

'BEING OF A SOUND AND DISPOSING MIND AND MEMORY'

THE LAST WILL AND TESTAMENT OF SAMUEL CHAPMAN

In his will Samuel gave £200 to each of the Norwich Hospitals.

He left a substantial legacy in augmentation of the church of Metfield (a donative in Suffolk) where he held lands, and ordered his tenements and copy-hold lands there to be sold (over £520) to be laid out in freehold lands, with a convenient house for the use of the minister.

He left forty-five acres of copy-hold land at Brundall, in trust, the rent thereof for the education of six poor children in the parish of Thorpe, including a salary for a schoolmaster.

And:

> ... 13s 4d for a sermon to be preached annually on 6th January
> ... 1s 8d to the parish clerk
> ... 11s to the poor in bread

His beloved books he had willed to me, for he knew how I loved to be surrounded by all that knowledge. The remainder of Samuel's estate, the '... other charitable purposes not specified...', also passed to me. It was a substantial amount of money and I was thankful for his foresight. Thankful that I did not need to fall back on the generosity of family, as so many poor widows were forced to do, or to suffer that most terrible of fates, to live out my days in the poorhouse. No, I was at least spared that. I was a widow, but a wealthy widow, and thus I was able to make choices about my future. But for the first time in my life I was without the protection of my father, or my husband, and henceforth I would have to make my own way.

I had to leave the rectory, the beloved home I had shared for almost twenty years with Samuel. In my grief I had not even considered that I would have to move, but I was informed, with undue haste, I felt, that it was required immediately by the new rector. But, truly, what did I expect? Some time to adjust to my loss before having to leave the house where we had been so very happy? Some acknowledgement of my loss, even? Some understanding that the happiest years of my life had been spent within those walls? Well, yes, I did, I expected all that, and some basic kindness. But it was not to be – the church needed a new rector, and the new rector needed our house. With nothing to lose and determined I would have the time to say goodbye, I stalled. Though my mind was fogged with grief, I remembered the worthy gentlemen who had attended my father's funeral, and Samuel's, and the promise they had made to help me should I ever be in need. I wrote a short note to the one who seemed the most kind and he was able to use his own connections, and Samuel's good name, to persuade the bishop to grant me a few days' grace in which to gather my memories, to pack our belongings and to say farewell.

I found some strength in the days after Samuel's death, resolute that I would find a way to carry on without him and build a fitting legacy to his kind heart and to our love, but, I confess, leaving our little rectory nearly broke me. For those all too few days that I had been allowed, I locked the door, closed the windows and asked that nobody call on me. Shut away it was the strangest of times, just me, Samuel's possessions and my memories. I was strangely content, soaking up what little I had left of him but also knowing that leaving would take me further away from my beloved, away from our precious life together. I sat for hours in the rooms we shared, night and day, reliving our lives and remembering those times over and over, as much as I could bear. I stood at each window, looking out onto our garden, the river, his church, the graveyard, knowing I would not forget those sights but also knowing with sadness that they would never be as strong as in that moment – that my memories would dim and fade.

Though I spent much of that time just sitting and looking and thinking, I had somehow managed to pack up all our belongings. I had asked Samuel's good friends to clear his study and to take a book each in his memory, and I donated the others to Norwich Library. I kept one great pile of books that I knew he had treasured, and, of course, the ones we had shared, though I could not bear to even look at them. I buried them deep amongst his clothes, in his battered and carved oak chest. On that last afternoon I left the trunks and boxes and chests containing all of our life together at the end of the path, where I had arranged for them to be collected and moved to my new lodgings, along with a few pieces of furniture. For now, I was going to a smaller house, suitable and clean, just along the river – not our rectory, our home, but, still, close by. I had assured well-meaning friends and family that truly I did want to be alone, to say my final goodbye. I went from room to room, for the very last time, feeling the whole of my body trembling. Needing all of my strength to move my legs, I had to force myself from one room to the next. Finally, knowing I had to leave while I still had some hold on myself, I walked, stalked, through the kitchen door and outside. That door, which had connected our lives together in our little rectory with our lives in his church nearby. That door, the one I had opened to welcome him home for so many nights and had closed behind him to keep us safe, to keep us together. But then, on that last day, having pulled it shut behind me for the final time and believing I was over the worst, I thought I would stay for a while in our garden. There, on the little stone wall where Samuel used to sit and watch me, I sat and scraped out the moss and tiny weeds that had grown in the short time since Samuel had last pulled them out, whistling on his way to church. Warmed by the sun, I stopped only when my nails became torn and sore, placing my fingers in my mouth to stem the seeping blood. I looked up and I saw the rosemary bushes where I used to drape our clothes to air, and I saw the wild flowers that had spread their joyous colour all around, and our beautiful roses, our treasured rosa mundi, planted with love – the swirled and striped petals, crimson and pink and white, a wonder to us. I was hit, stunned, by the realisation that I would never see them again. I would never again savour the soft sweet scent of those heavenly roses. I leant forward and pulled a handful of those glorious crimson and pink and white petals and pushed them into my pocket, wanting to keep their perfect beauty. I was struck, too, that it would be another person who next entered this garden and that they would benefit from all our loving care – from all that beauty. Then I was overcome by a fear that they might not see what we saw, that they might not love our beautiful walled garden, and that in a few months it would become overgrown, neglected, as though wiping away the last traces of Samuel and me, and our lives lived as one. The tears came, and I sobbed, great heaving torrents of tears, noisy and uncontrolled, as though my body was forcing me to cry out all of my grief. Just for a moment I had a demented desire, that I might somehow stop the world, turn back time, to be allowed to stay, even for one more day. Should I return to the rectory and barricade the door? My mind, still then a sound and disposing mind, shook me back to reality with a heavy dread, and I was left with a great weight of feeling, knowing that life had changed and that I could not stay. Finally, drained, I realised that I was causing myself more pain the longer I stayed. I pushed myself off the wall and marched, as upright as I could manage, down the path, through the little wooden gate, through the fronds of our willow tree, and away.

In those long months after Samuel's death I simply carried on living; there was nothing else I could do. I regained my poise, outwardly at least. I had a role, the respected widow of that most loved and most pious of ministers, Samuel Chapman. I carried on visiting the parishioners, even attending the church services, once again making polite, empty conversation with the great and the good of the parish. While talking, though, I was careful to keep my back to the rectory, not wanting to see what had become of our little garden, or to see that door, behind which all of my happiness had lain.

I was once again just Mary, almost my younger self, lonely and unloved Mary. Devout and conscientious Mary. Kind and caring (or so I appeared), though I did not feel it in my heart. Outwardly I continued to do good, and in that way, I managed to get through the long hours of those long days. Each night, however, in my lodgings, finally and thankfully alone and where I no longer had to pretend, the tears fell as soon as I had closed the door. In later days, when my tears had exhausted me, I simply sat, and found I had a cold, black soul. No longer able to remember those precious memories I had tried so hard to hold on to, not even trying to remember – not thinking at all. Certainly not thinking of the hospital I had faithfully promised to build as testament to Samuel's goodness. No. I just sat, still dressed in my widow's black. I had barely unpacked, only those items that were essential for my basic, joyless life. My heavily curtained rooms were cold, dark and empty, and I liked it that way.

In one corner of the room, Samuel's clothes and the possessions he had cherished, his prayer book and his *Pilgrim's Progress*, were locked away in his old oak chest, a few rose petals scattered amongst them. Crushed and faded. Crimson and pink and white.

But I am a survivor, and little by little I saw signs that I might emerge from my grief. I simply got fed up with sitting in the gloom and I lit a fire at night; the warmth and the glow got me moving and I started to unpack. I rediscovered a treasured shawl, a gift from my father, made on his looms, the finest wool and the deepest green, shot through with bright gold threads. I wrapped it around myself, which somehow helped to block out the worst of the loneliness. I made up the bed and slept there for the first time since I had moved in, and I slept well. The next day I rose early and went outside to pull up some of the valerian plants I had glimpsed growing in the damp hedgerow near the river. I forced down an earthy tea made from their roots, which seemed to calm some of my anxieties. I got busy and washed the windows and swept the path and cut back the weeds, and I found the energy to make myself some nourishing broth. I carried on with my daily rounds, still caring for others but now with more genuine concern, and I noticed some of my former kindness returning. I still preferred to be by myself in the evenings, still exhausted and not needing any company or conversation. I tried hard to ward off some of our former parishioners and so avoid their fussing and advice. I did not see it at the time, and they only irritated me with their concern, but it was simply that they did not know what to do to help, and their visits were their way of showing that I was not alone. I was unable to completely avoid one or two of them, who sometimes popped up if I ventured into the garden for a little air, as if they had been waiting for me to surface. They had even dared to comment, a little cautiously, for my temper was quick to flare, that I was looking a little better, and they were rewarded for their bravery and optimism with a dark frown. I fear that I was not at my best in those times.

I was not quite free of unwanted visitors, for then my brother called, bringing a formal offer of marriage from the odious man who had cornered me, twice, as I had mourned. I was silent for a few moments, quite unable to express how horrified I was at such a prospect, while my brother, impatient, insisted that it was a good proposition and I should be grateful. Tired and just wanting to be left alone, I found my voice and informed him, at some length, that I would not marry again and certainly not to someone who was chosen for me. Realising that it would help my brother's own business interests to have that loathsome man married into our family, I continued to argue, stating that I did not care to be treated in such a way, and that he should take my refusal and make it clear that it was my final answer. He left, annoyed. Later, I realised that I had not thought to be polite, or hide my feelings, and, though it took a while to calm myself, I felt good.

That night I awoke suddenly, hearing Sam call to me, loud and clear. I heard his voice, my name, 'Mary… Mary…' He was in my room. I was certain he was in my room, looking over me. But, of course, he was not; he could not be. I was saddened, then, for it was a cruel reminder of all I had lost, but the next morning his voice was still strong inside me and I was comforted. I am, after all, a most sensible woman, with no time for stories of spirits or apparitions, but I am still firm in my belief that I truly heard his voice. I understood then that my memory of him would always be with me – I would never forget him and that gave me peace. I opened the chest containing his belongings, noticing anew where the lid had been worn smooth by years of the touch of his fingers. I inhaled the faint perfume of the slither of my own rose-scented soap that I had thrown in simply because it had been his hands that had touched it last. I pulled out a few of his books and placed them on a window sill, just to be there, in sight and in reach. But then later that evening I picked one up and I read a few short sentences, and soon I dozed in my chair, happy, almost, knowing that he had turned those pages. Other nights I sat, and with uneven stitches I slowly mended his shirts. Later, I delivered them, washed and folded, to the poorhouse, where I knew they would be worn by some of the residents – I think Samuel would have liked that. I polished his boots, burnished black and soft, shaped by his feet, for he had walked miles in those boots, over so many years. How many times had I chatted to him as he sat and bent to unlace them when he returned home to me? And now I wondered how he had managed to get his great gnarled feet, his beautiful feet, with toes the colour of parchment, into such beautiful boots. I left them at the side of the fireplace, the laces trailing. Visitors commented, of course, but I assured them I was not mad; I knew he was gone, that he would not return and put them on. It shocked me a little that they thought I was so far gone in my senses. But that simple act, that acknowledgement that he would always be a part of my life, that I did not have to keep his memory packed away, seemed to free me from the worst of my grief, and it enabled me to live a little more peacefully.

I visited his grave often, too often perhaps for those insensitive people who advised me to consider getting remarried, but still I would walk there in the afternoons, knowing somehow that it was bad for me to be confined in the gloom of the house for too long. One day, as I stood in the church, the sun shone through the windows and lit the air, and I was irritated to see all the dust circling about and settling onto his tombstone. I could not see a broom and I did not wish to seek anyone out to ask for one, so I bent down to wipe his grave with my handkerchief. A little piece of ribbon by the wall caught my eye, and I recognised it from the posy left by that poor soldier's mother – the ribbon now a grubby grey and covered in dust. I remembered then that she, a frail and poor woman, had walked miles on the day of Samuel's funeral, from Norwich to Thorpe and back, to pay her respects. How I had been too caught up in my own grief to have any consideration for her then. Hurrying back to my kitchen I put together a parcel of some lace-thin slices of beef, a quarter of my soft buttery cheese and a bottle of heartsease tonic, all wrapped up in a clean cloth. I called to one of the boys who passed by looking for odd jobs and instructed him to deliver it to her. I was firm: he had to make sure to put it in her hands and return to me, when I would pay him a few extra pennies. He duly reported that she had been suspicious at first, but he had told her it was from 'Mrs Chapman, the rector's widow woman' and only then would she take it from him. She had stated, 'Please thank Mrs Chapman for her kindness,' and closed the door. I told him to return that day each week to do the same, and he turned up, unfailingly.

It is strange, but truly I cannot recall with any detail what happened in the seven or so years that passed after Samuel's death. I know I am indebted to my friend Hannah, who visited me regularly during those long years. Hannah had been married to my older brother, Robert, and after his early death she became well acquainted with the life of a widow. She took care not to criticise my brother, but I had an inkling that theirs was not an entirely happy union, and, after the accepted period of mourning, she was quite able to continue with her life without showing too much distress. She was being courted by Francis Keeling, a local merchant, who, I heard was a decent man, and I wished her a lifetime of happiness. I am forever grateful for Hannah's thoughtfulness in that dark time, for I suspect I was not easy company. I was bereft, drowning, and she must have needed all her patience to keep returning to my sad house, and my miserable face, for all that time. It is a wonder to me how sometimes the most unexpected people shine through. When she was married to my brother, Hannah and I saw each other only rarely, mostly at church and family gatherings. I confess, I had little time for her for I had assumed, quite incorrectly, as it turns out, that she was one of those downtrodden married women who existed only to support their husbands. I remember, however, that she took the trouble to say some kind words to me at my father's funeral, and that she was visibly upset at his passing. Amidst all the sympathy that I had struggled to tolerate at Samuel's funeral, it was her offer of help that I remembered most clearly, as well as her kindness in the time that followed. She came by the rectory each day and left a little basket of simple fresh food on the doorstep, to tempt and sustain me through that horrible time. She was one of the few people who made good on their offer of help and she has been a constant source of support ever since my great loss. Hannah seemed to know that I needed to be left alone to grieve for much longer than was considered normal. But that was my way, and she kept a quiet presence, understanding that I would not always want to be so alone.

With Hannah's support I slowly accepted that my life would continue, whether I wished it or not, until God chose to take me. My life was mundane, and quite uneventful, but I was once again busy. I saw that I had spent far too long being idle, that great sin. It appears that when I was in the depths of my grief and I had struggled to care for myself, it had been decided by my brothers that I was not well enough to look after Ellen. But, when it came to an offer of any practical help, they had all produced quite ready reasons for not being able to take Ellen into their own homes. Hannah, my saviour yet again, with a great kindness that I can never repay, had taken Ellen in during those months when I had been at my most desperate. I am ashamed to say that I had neglected my sister, but she had accepted that she would live with Hannah until I recovered my health. My grief was an illness that Ellen could not comprehend, and she insisted that she should visit me every few days to check on me, perhaps also to reassure herself that I would not suddenly disappear, as our mother had. But, as had happened throughout her life, my sister's illness worsened every few years, and she was once again showing signs of great agitation, so much so that Hannah was starting to struggle to persuade Ellen to return home with her after their visits. Thankfully, I was emerging from my grief, and I could see the distress the visits were causing both Hannah and Ellen, and I suggested that Ellen could come and live with me once again.

We moved to a larger house, still close to the river, in sight of Samuel's church, but on a little hill, in a quieter area, which was better for Ellen. I declined to have servants to help with the running of the house, knowing Ellen preferred there to be only the two of us, but I sent our laundry out, and I arranged for a delivery of provisions from the market each week. And I could always ask my new friend, the young lad who took my weekly parcel to the soldier's mother, who would reliably appear whenever I needed an errand to be run. After a few months of quite demanding behaviour Ellen finally quietened again, and we settled into a more or less peaceful companionship.

It was Hannah who brought my copies of the *Norwich Post*, our very own city newspaper, printed at the Red Well in Norwich. Looking through it kept me busy in the evenings, and often I would read out loud to Ellen, though it contained little of interest to her. Still, we liked to sit side by side, and I found those nights together eased some of my sadness. Ellen even laughed a little as I struggled to hold my new eye-glasses on my nose with one hand and the newspaper in the other, as she waited to see which one I would inevitably drop first. The print in the newspapers was so small I simply would not have been able to read without my eye-glasses, and, despite my usual thriftiness, I considered them a worthy investment, though I suppose they were a luxury. I cared not if they made me look old, as Ellen mischievously suggested, for that is what I had become. My once-glorious hair had a streak of grey at the front, and it only took a few moments to tuck it under my cap. I still dressed in my widow's black for I could not find the energy to be fitted for anything new. I had given away my clothes from my years with Samuel, unable to look at myself in them. I saved only the dress that Samuel had loved most, the deep green taffeta, and even that was consigned to the bottom of his chest, for its rich colour no longer suited my faded face.

Much of the newspaper was filled with tedious reports of the city council meetings, which I did not read out, but there was also news from further afield. I read the full description of the death of our king, William of Orange, who had been distraught at the passing of his beloved wife, years before. The ringing of the bells throughout the country to signal the king's grief is still tied up in my mind with the death of my father. I also recalled that I still had Samuel beside me at that time, to help me through my grief – I had not even considered that I would lose him, or that I would ever have to live without him. And, though I was entirely restored in my sound and disposing mind, and I had accepted that he was gone and that I could not follow, why, then, did I still, on occasion, think that I could hear him coming through the door as the night grew dark? I was a sensible woman, not usually given to fanciful thoughts, so why did I wish with all my being that it were possible? But time helps to heal the heart, and the mind, or at least, time softens the pain. I no longer had to stop suddenly and stand in the street while I gathered my senses, having caught the perfume of the roses that were so popular, and that still remind me of the time of his death. And as each summer passed I had become, if not used to these feelings, then at least a little more prepared.

Word had spread that I was well enough to take care of my troubled sister, and therefore people assumed I could also help them with their own difficulties, and so, once again, I was in demand. There were many families who tried to care at home for loved ones who had been temporarily deprived of their reason. Quite often, with time, gentle care and understanding, many eventually returned to their senses. For the most part my role was to visit regularly and support their exhausted, anxious kin and to advise against the more barbaric so-called cures recommended by some of our medical men. A few of the younger doctors, and many of those who cared daily for the afflicted, doubted that mental debility could be purged from the body. Certainly, regular bleeding seemed only to make patients worse, and the mere appearance of some of the most notorious doctors would cause cold fear in the disturbed, thereby prompting the very behaviours that they were attempting to cure. I am heartened that our simple approach of kindness and time helped many, but I admit that we were not always successful. The most severely deranged were quite often a danger to themselves and to those who cared for them. I was sometimes called to help those poor wretches, often as a last resort, when their desperate family did not know what else to do. Sadly, for many of the violent or unpredictable lunaticks, there was an inevitable admission to one of the private hospitals, where they could be kept secure. Though a few were good places, many others were less so, but there was little alternative. Throughout this time, I was always looking for answers, and taking note of which manifestations of madness we made progress with and those we could hope to cure. I was kept busy, unable to turn down a request for help where I thought I could be of use, and I was too tired to think much of anything at the end of each day, and for that, at least, I was grateful.

THREE OLD MAIDS IN A PHYSICK GARDEN

The good times did return, however, at least often enough to give me hope that I could endure the rest of my days. We still saw Hannah. She visited, and when the weather was pleasant we would all sit together on my garden bench and point out the herbs and healing plants that were starting to flourish all around us in my new physick garden – and we giggled, remembering the stealth by which it had been created…

A few months earlier, when it had seemed that I was at last emerging from my grief, I had had a brief crying fit one day, prompted by remembering the garden I had created with Samuel and regretting that I had left so many plants and herbs behind. I was once again visiting those in need of care, and I had a demand for the calming teas, tonics, balms and nourishing possets that I had previously prepared with herbs from our garden. Now I was cross with myself that I hadn't thought, in those last days at the rectory, to gather some seeds. Of course, I had been in such a wretched state that I had been barely capable of rational thought, let alone able to look to the future, but still I was angry at overlooking something that now seemed so important. Hannah suggested we ask for cuttings from the parishioners' gardens as many of our plants grew quite freely, but I insisted, quite petulantly, I'm afraid, that I wanted only those I had planted during my time with Samuel. Taking a breath, Hannah then tried to persuade me to ask the new rector if I could visit the garden again and collect some cuttings and seeds, but I refused, knowing that I could never return to the happy home that had been such a precious part of my previous life.

The following Sunday we visited Samuel's church at Thorpe as usual and, after the service, Hannah instructed me to keep the rector busy with conversation and prevent him from returning to the rectory, and she and Ellen darted off. I did as I was bid, and I suffered many long minutes engaged in possibly the most tedious conversation of my life. Forgive me, Lord. Well, in truth, I was forced mostly to listen to that dreadful, dour man, for he gave me no opportunity to venture an opinion. I was also aware that he kept glancing over my shoulder seeking someone more important to give his opinions to, but I was too polite to comment. I was horribly distracted by the rank foulness of the fug emanating from his mouth, and I was considering offering him some of my clove tooth powder to sweeten his breath. But just in time, just as I was about to throw myself to the ground in defeat, I felt Ellen at my elbow, looking a little flushed and excited. She tugged at my arm and I made my excuses as we hurried down the path, to find Hannah waiting for us at the little church gate.

They were both quite silly on the way home, and I was starting to think they had been to the White Lion for a secret mug of ale. However, once we were behind the wall of my new garden, they showed me the contents of their pockets, overflowing with the seeds of the plants and herbs and flowers from our old rectory garden. Whilst I had stood, suffering at the mouth of the rector, they had climbed over the gate and had run around pulling off as many seed heads as they could grab, piling them into their pockets, tucking them into their skirts and wrapping the larger ones in a headscarf. Their plan had gone well until they were walking down the path from the rectory to the church, where they had met one of the church wardens who was eyeing them with suspicion, about to question their conduct. While Hannah had tried to stutter an explanation, my darling Ellen had put on the most convincing display of impending hysteria and he had changed his countenance immediately and anxiously escorted them back to the church.

When we had ceased laughing at their daring tale and regained our composure, I looked at the bounty in front of me, almost taken from God's own garden. Lavender, camomile and rue, fennel, mint and lemon balm, even some cuttings of our precious roses. I could have cried at their kindness, but for once, and rarely for me, I grabbed them both and hugged them, so filled with joy that I had regained the essence of our precious garden, and a little piece of my life with Samuel. Our love could indeed endure. I spent many happy days after that, planting and tending those seeds, watching them sprout and spread, feeling my heart fill with Samuel once more as they grew. Now I could dare to remember the joyous times of my life, for I was once again in full possession of the sound and disposing mind and memory that I had been so assured of for all of my life.

I was a little troubled that Hannah had involved Ellen in her plan, but it seems Ellen had been perfectly content to take such a risk and had experienced a little joy and freedom that day as she darted about the garden. Ellen quietly explained to me that she had spent her whole life being stared at and treated as an outsider, so, even if they had been caught, how could the words of people who already looked down on her do her any further harm? My, how I loved her for that, but it filled me with sadness, too, that she had lived her whole life fully aware of how different she was, and even we, her family who loved her, had not understood the true depths of her torment at all. Ellen took much comfort from our garden after that, spending more time outside, even when her dark moods started to descend once again. She would also, on those occasions when she could sense that I was a little sad, place a few wildflowers in my room, often forgetting that they needed water to survive. Still, such kindness, when I needed it most.

So, we sat, us three, in the physick garden, looking to the passers-by like plain, respectable, contented old maids. If they only knew.

'A MONUMENT OF MY THANKFULNESS'

As each year passed, I celebrated Plough Monday, listening devotedly to the sermon that Samuel had specified in his will, and I diligently attended church each week, but at last I reacquainted myself with God, truly and in my heart. I was, once again, able to commit fully to my visits to the needy, and I considered my new endeavours at providing succour to the afflicted as my means of serving God. I was relieved to live my life for Him once again, gaining a new strength and determination. I had settled into my grief, still occasionally struck by my shattering loss, but for the most part able to remember my time with Samuel with joy, and to continue with the life I had been blessed with. I no longer felt guilty if I was able to laugh, despite my grief, for Sam had loved to see me laugh. He himself had been, despite his serious and scholarly appearance, a bit of a giggler, though only in my presence, whenever the opportunity presented itself.

As I lived my life with joy once again and with my memories of Samuel strong within me, I was content to wait until God chose to reunite us. And praise be to God, the only wise God, for He had restored me to my sound and disposing mind, and as a monument of my thankfulness for this invaluable mercy I committed the remainder of my life to Him.

It had been noticed that I had, at last, regained my true sense of self and, horrifyingly, my brother made another attempt at finding a suitor for me, so that I would not be alone in my later years, but I had firmly subdued any suggestion of a further marriage. As if I would wish to be saddled with some tedious, tired old man – I already had an excess of people in need of my devotion without adding another. I was quite stern in my rejection of such a terrible idea, and rather quickly he saw that I would not be persuaded and sensibly he let me be. I did not need to explain this time, a firm 'no', uttered only once, was sufficient. And, quite honestly, who could match my beloved Sam, he who had made me whole? I had experienced the most beautiful love with the kindest of men, and I would be content with that for the rest of my days.

Seven

ONE THOUSAND YEARS AND A PEPPERCORN RENT

I approached my sixtieth year, appearing, perhaps, an old woman, for grief had aged me. I was busy and no longer lonely, but still alone, and accepting that I would see out my remaining time on earth quietly, if God granted it. But in that year I had cause to rethink my life.

I had my annual meeting with the trustees of the remainder of Samuel's estate. I had been able to live comfortably for the past seven years, and I had provided a pleasant home for my sister where she could feel secure, but the trustees informed me that I had barely touched the bulk of Samuel's bequest. I had attended this meeting every January since his death, but clearly I had not listened, or it would not have come as quite such a shock to hear that Samuel's legacy had been well managed and invested by his trustees and there was now a substantial sum, more than I would ever require in my lifetime. I left the meeting a little dazed, but truly I had no time for such wealth. I had sufficient for my needs and I did not require any more possessions, or ornaments. I thought, perhaps, I would leave some money in trust for the care of my sister, Ellen, should I predecease her, and a bequest to Hannah, my most faithful of friends. Content with that decision, I paid no more attention to the matter, for a while at least.

Later that year, 1707, the *Norwich Post* was full of all the details of 'an event of historic national importance'. I read the reports of the celebrations (and a few protests) that accompanied the signing of the new Act of Union. That momentous Act had succeeded in finally uniting the Parliaments of England and Scotland into one Parliament of Great Britain. The Act of Union had been one of the policies fought for by Queen Anne, as she sought a solution to benefit all. Since her accession to the throne in 1702, she had proposed greater political integration, which, as far as I could see, though I, too, was a mere woman, let us not forget, could only lead to a more peaceful country. The more I read of our queen, the more I was starting to admire her, though she was often treated unkindly in the newspapers, with her close female friendships and endless, fruitless pregnancies. I had paid little attention to politics in the depths of my grief, but I was struck that it was a woman, Queen Anne, who had finally united our two warring countries. She gave us the prospect of peace, though many, looking after their own interests, perhaps, continued to be opposed to the Union. The truth was that the previous rule of kings and the Lord Protectors and the Parliaments, all men of course, had only resulted in year after year of turbulence, war and unnecessary death. Could it be that the Union had been achieved because of the persistence and patience of a woman, the often-derided Queen Anne? And, if so, could an ordinary woman, like me, also have influence, or even achieve great change? I mused on this for a good while. But then my mundane, busy life took over, I forgot my lofty thoughts and I became, once again, fully occupied with the daily demands for my ministrations. I attended Dorothy's funeral, for she had died aged fifty-eight, yet another poor soul I had outlived, but I carried on, I persisted, for what else was there to do, until God decided it was my time?

I made my customary visit to Samuel's grave on the anniversary of our marriage. But this time, as I sat in our little church, as close to him as I could be, I was aware of an energy forming, replacing the dragging sadness that I usually let surround me, if only for the time I spent unobserved, by his side. As I rose to leave him, saying a quiet, 'Farewell, my joy and rest', I heard a young couple enter the church. Thinking they were alone, they were holding hands, and I moved towards the wall, not wanting my gloomy face to spoil their happiness. They drew close together to whisper something that made them both giggle, and almost skipped down the nave and swung their hands, as if with the joy of children, perfectly happy with each other and in their own little world. I quietly left the church and couldn't help but smile. Sam would have loved that moment – some reassurance that the world would survive for as long as young people were free to love and delight in each other. Samuel and I had met later in life, so we were never young as a couple, but we had loved, and we had giggled; we had even held hands, though never in public.

I was reminded of the church meetings we used to attend, which were such a dreary experience that we both dreaded them, though of course we did our duty and attended and behaved with all seriousness. One evening, though, we had entered the church together, full of love and life, and then I had sat and watched as Samuel's shoulders slumped lower and lower towards the table as the meeting progressed. Those tedious discussions seemed interminable, until Samuel looked up and made some comment that didn't quite fit, something and nothing, really, but it had struck a part of me, and as I caught his eye I knew he had felt it too. I had to leave at once for fear of embarrassing him with my laughter. I managed a polite excuse of needing some air and hurried away and hid amongst the fronds of our favourite willow tree, where I was free to laugh out loud. I just could not control myself, repeating Sam's comment in my head, and, as I pictured the bemused faces of the church worthies, another fit of giggling would come over me. I was still struggling to calm myself when Sam appeared, red-faced with the effort of trying to contain himself, having left the church under the pretence of seeing if I was unwell. We ran back to our rectory, still laughing, and fell on the door as we closed it behind us, free to laugh together until we were weak, free from the disapproving glares of the stern church committee, who looked as if they would not know a laugh if it peered over their shoulder. For years afterwards, just his comment, just a glance between us, could set us both off, uncontrolled, maybe a little hysterical, but also just filled with pure joy.

'FOR ALL AND EVERY OF THESE REASONS'

I yearned for him then, remembering – that understanding, that connection of souls, somehow more enduring even than love. Feeling the loneliness of knowing it could never happen to me again and the happiness of having experienced it at all. That night I sat up late, still struck by the young couple, happy and alive and together, and, thinking of Samuel, I also remembered my promise to him, a promise that had been hidden for years, submerged by my grief, but a promise nonetheless, and one I knew I had to keep – to create a place of safety for the poor lunaticks of our city, to build his Bethel as a monument to our love. I remembered the surge of energy I had experienced in the church, and felt the start of something, at first simply a thought that, despite my age and my ailments, perhaps it was still possible. Remembering, too, the example of Queen Anne, her dogged determination and her will to get things done. She was a queen and thus a powerful woman, yet she was often cruelly ridiculed, for she was still a woman in a world run by men, but she had found her strength, and clearly she did not allow the bad grace and ambitions of others get in her way.

My new-found inspiration, my energy, my certainty were tempered by one thought which troubled me greatly. How could I have not carried out his dearest wish? How could I have left it for so long? And why, oh, why, had I not started all this years ago, when I had been a little more youthful, when my bones creaked less? My only defence was that I could remember so little of the time since his death, my mind numbed by grief and my body weakened by the loss of his physical presence. Perhaps, too, I was distracted by the need to care for Ellen, and to do my duty to all those who needed me. Yet, still, I had to consider it – his legacy. It would have to be perfect if it was to reflect my love for him. So, was it easier to not try at all than to try and fail? And, if I failed, what sort of memorial to our love would that be? Confused and overcome with tiredness, I climbed into bed and got under the covers. As my mind quietened, another memory came to me, of my walk along the riverbank after Samuel's funeral, and suddenly, as strong as it had been all those years before, I regained my belief that somehow, with God's grace, and with Samuel's love still within me, I would build his Bethel. It was possible – it had to be.

Well, if faith and love were all that were needed, then I should achieve it all. But, despite my energy and my determination, it seemed it was not a simple matter, and I met with many hurdles that I could not have foreseen. Immediately, though, I made plans. I met with Samuel's trustees again and instructed them to prepare to release funds from his rental properties so that they would be available when I found a suitable building for my hospital. They were clearly amused and advised me against buying a property for such an unusual use – a folly, as one called it. They all talked at me at once, saying that my wealth would only continue to grow if I were to leave it with them, and then they repeated themselves, as if I had not grasped their words the first time. As I stood to leave, I looked at each one in turn and reminded them that, according to my most beloved husband's wishes, his legacy was now mine to use as I saw fit. They all looked at me, clearly surprised that I had finally spoken up, although not quite as surprised as I was, and I had to quickly turn away, so they couldn't see my reddening face.

I realised that I might need some support and I remembered the promises made at my father's funeral, but, sadly, I found that many of his old friends had since died. One or two of their sons kindly agreed to help me when I found a suitable building, though I was a little disappointed that some of them appeared to take me not altogether seriously. Perhaps Queen Anne felt the same as she fought to make herself heard. Still, I wrote to all the land agents in the area, detailing the type of building I was looking for and asking them to inform me as soon as suitable premises became available. But every one of them failed to respond, though perhaps I should not have been surprised by their reaction. I was forced again to look for further favours and I asked Augustus Bush, the son of one of my father's fellow aldermen, to contact the land agents on my behalf. This he did, although he was a little bemused, I felt, by this determined little woman in black, particularly as I stridently demanded that those men, who were clearly of limited imagination, must, nevertheless, take me and my vision seriously.

Whilst I… he… we… waited for a reply, I started to write out plans for the care of the lunaticks that would one day become resident in my hospital, plans of how they would be treated, who I would need to employ, what rooms we required, and even the drawings of a small garden. I worked for many months on those plans while we waited, adding improvements here and there, until, finally, we were offered a few buildings to view. I was excited to see them, thinking that I would turn a corner and the Bethel would appear before me, in bricks and mortar. I was accompanied by Mr Bush, who I'm pleased to say was starting to treat me less like a mad old aunt and more as a fellow human being and, at times, even as someone with sensible and serious thoughts. He managed a few intelligent questions himself, though he was quite lacking any semblance of a sense of humour. Of course, I am forever grateful for his time and attention, for I would have failed at this first step without his presence.

To my annoyance, those first properties were all unsuitable – great wrecks of places, much too costly to convert and certainly not fit accommodation for my lunaticks. It turned out that they were the buildings that no one else was interested in. Mr Bush, who could probably foresee himself trudging in my wake for years without end, got himself moving and insisted that the land agents should offer us some less dilapidated properties, but still there was nothing suitable. Then Mr Bush suggested, a little desperately perhaps, that maybe I should start to draw up outline plans for building a completely new hospital, and we began another search for a piece of land that was large enough and near to Thorpe. A few weeks later we had some success. We were offered the lease of a large house, surrounded by grounds, all set within a high wall. It was just perfect, for I could see Samuel's church from the window of one of the second-floor rooms. I could be close to him and he could watch over us. Our (Mr Bush's) offer seemed to be progressing, but then it was abruptly and irrevocably withdrawn. I surmised it was because the so-called great and good of the area did not want to live too close to lunaticks – the fearful tales of the Bedlam still causing suspicion and distress – and, yes, they had indeed put pressure on the landowner not to lease to us. They did not even have the grace to give their true reasons, saying instead that they were concerned that the Reverend Chapman's widow was showing signs of mental debility herself and was not well enough to succeed in such an undertaking. Mr Bush looked quite shamefaced as he reported this to me, but I thanked him, not only for his endeavours on my behalf but also for continuing to represent me. I was disappointed, for I had quite moved in already, but, more importantly, it was time wasted, and at my age I resented that greatly. There was nothing to be done, but this experience served to strengthen my resolve, for I had started to see what I was truly up against.

We found another house, smaller than I had been hoping for but quite new and with a beautiful garden, but the owner, set in his own views of the role of women, declined to sell to me, or, should I say, declined to sell to my trustees on my behalf when he realised that a woman would be in charge. As we left the land agent's office, I muttered to myself, with some venom, about the owner's lack of compassion, and even Mr Bush made a few choice remarks.

I was so riled by the owner's attitude that, when I unexpectedly came across him, some weeks later, after a church service in Norwich, I stood in his path, so that he could not avoid me. I stood as tall as I could, though I still only reached up to his armpits, and I tried one of my father's intimidating growls. 'I do hope, sir, that as someone who clearly lacks our good Lord's compassion, you are never in need of my charity. Good-day.' He looked rather startled as he peered down at me, and I was quite pleased at my bravery for I had clearly put him in his place. Later, I realised he probably had no idea who I was or what I was talking about. But I cared not, for I was getting old, and it seemed that with age came the ability to truly speak one's mind.

As more time passed, I reflected on those early difficulties with some disbelief. I was becoming frustrated at continually having to explain, to justify myself, and I was angry at being turned away time after time, simply for being a woman, as if that made me incapable of making a sensible decision. Even though Queen Anne had to fight to be taken seriously, I doubt even she had that much trouble. Perhaps I needed a royal patron; maybe then people would help me, without that look of disbelief spreading across their faces, as they understood that it was a woman, an old woman, who wanted to do all this. But I did not have a royal patron, and thus I did the only thing I knew to do – I prayed, and I persevered. *Per ardua stabilis.* I had been a determined little girl, and I had learnt from the example of my mother to stand my ground when it was important. The ways of the world had not changed as much as I would have liked in the previous fifty years, but I was resolute, for I would not let Samuel down.

There is much to be said for growing old, though it also has its drawbacks. But I had nothing to lose; I would build the Bethel in my remaining years, or I would die. It was as simple as that. Whatever pleased God. I prayed to Him to guide me and I received no sign that He wanted me to stop. In fact, my bones ached a little less and my head was clear, so I continued to make plans. All the while I was still caring for Ellen and others I had collected along the way. Each evening I worked and reworked my designs for the Bethel. I thanked God for giving my father the sense to allow his daughters to learn to write, as well as read, and for blessing me with the gift of perseverance. It had served me well, as a child when I was studying those tedious texts with my tutor, and in my later years when I needed all my reserves to continue with my mission against such annoying opposition.

Early one evening, after another gloomy, dank day, the rain finally stopped and I put the plans aside and walked into my garden to attempt to order my thoughts. And I paced. Was there something else I could do? What was stopping me from realising my dream? What would Samuel advise me to do? But no answers appeared and the rain fell again; there was not even a glimpse of a rainbow to encourage me. I stood still for a while, but then returned to the house, damp and a little defeated. As I patted my hair dry I thought again of my desire to build a caring, secure hospital where we could attempt to grant peace to the poor lunaticks of Norwich. I could hardly comprehend that there were men in our city who opposed me, but I knew that certain people preferred lunaticks to be locked away, or dumped outside the city walls, out of sight. I had some support – word of my mission had spread and the families of some of the lunaticks I visited told of their desperation for me to succeed, but sadly few of them had any power in our city and none owned any property or land.

There were also signs that some of the great and the good were quietly pushing me aside. I began to notice small things, conversations getting shorter, backs being turned, and as wives dutifully followed their husband's lead, they, too, greeted me with less warmth. And yet, all would appear well if I were to meet them while in the company of those who remembered my father with affection, their presence granting me some protection.

I still had Samuel's legacy, more than I required, and I had my plans, pages of plans, but I simply could not find suitable premises, or anyone who was willing to sell to me and there, I am sad to relate, when I could plan no more, my quest stalled. Though several more years passed with no progress, and though I did not know how I was ever going to achieve it, the tragedy and suffering I continued to see all around me every day made me even more determined to fulfil Samuel's wish. And, as for being shunned, well, that bothered me not at all, as I reminded myself of my father's words from years ago – I was quite willing to remain unpopular, if only I could do good.

A PIECE OF WASTE LAND

Then, as sometimes happens, life offered up a possibility. I had attended the magnificent church of St Peter Mancroft, on one of my rare visits to Norwich. Unwilling to join the unwelcoming congregation for their usual social chit-chat after the service, I sat for a while, thinking quietly of Samuel and of our wedding day, and our love. The rector's wife had found me sitting alone and invited me to join her for some refreshments. As I had not seen her for some time, and finding her to be a good listener, I explained my purpose. I rambled on a bit, but when I had finished she rose and asked me to accompany her and we returned to the church, now deserted of God's faithful flock, to find her husband. We stood with him, as the light of the day shone on us through the immense stained-glass windows, and I repeated my plans – my vision. I was a little embarrassed this time, realising how it must sound, thinking that perhaps I must appear a little crazy. But they did not ridicule me, though they could have, a woman of more than sixty years old wanting to build such a place, in those times.

As they listened, and as I described my search for a suitable site, I could see them glance at one another and then suggest we take a walk. Rather perplexed, I left the church with them and strolled a little way towards the Chapel-Field, just inside the city walls. I was still chattering on, for I was eager to explain all my ideas, having found few people who would truly listen to me, when, a little abruptly, they stopped and we fell silent. Ahead of me I looked upon a desolate space, with crumbling buildings either side, overgrown by dark swathes of vegetation, but with remains of timber and stone still visible. For a few moments I did not understand, but they explained – it was the site of the former Committee House, razed to the ground by the Great Blowe of 1648 and left derelict for more than a half century. I was taken back to a time in my childhood as I had sat and listened to my father's compelling tale of his darkest memory, told only once. His account of the Great Blowe.

NINETY-EIGHT BARRELS OF GUNPOWDER

After waiting until my mother had finally agreed we were old enough to hear this disturbing part of the history of our city, my father began to talk one evening in April, telling us part of the story over several nights. Sitting with a pot of ale by his side, and with the oldest children around him (and the youngest, who had crept downstairs and crouched quietly at the back of the room so as not to be noticed and sent back to bed), he enthralled us all with his tale of that momentous riot and the great explosion that followed.

My father started his story in London, back in 1605, with Guy Fawkes and his failed plot. Even as children we attended a special church service to give thanks for the deliverance of our kingdom from those Catholic conspirators. My mother had, of course, forbidden us to take part in the processions that passed by our house as night descended. We could hear the rowdy and drunken cheers as an effigy of Guy Fawkes, stuffed with cats, was paraded through the streets, to be burnt on one of the crackling bonfires that were set all around the city. My brothers, who had told us of that cruel detail, usually watched from one of our windows as this spectacle passed by, but I sat with Ellen, singing hymns to calm her while trying to block out the image of those poor howling cats.

'But' – and here my father paused – 'Guy Fawkes had only thirty-six barrels of gunpowder to blow up the whole of the Houses of Parliament… so how many barrels do you think exploded in the Great Blowe of Norwich?' And we tried to guess, higher and higher, until my father eventually told us, as we sat, amazed: 'Ninety-eight!', then another pause, while we gasped, eyes and mouths wide open. 'Ninety-eight barrels of gunpowder all set off at once!' My brothers, being boys, liked this bit of the story best as they were at an age when they were impressed by explosions. But, as the darkness of the story unfolded, even they were silenced. I used to wonder if my father had exaggerated his tale, as was his wont, but as I got older and I learnt the full truth of the events of that night, I realised they were disturbing enough without the need for him to weave his usual magic.

THE GREAT BLOWE

In April 1648, in the midst of the Civil Wars, when I was just a year old, some prominent parliamentarians in Norwich presented a petition, subscribed to by about 150 people, to John Utting, the mayor. They were calling for a more speedy and thorough reformation of the Church, moving away from the Catholic religion. But the mayor took no notice of their demands and refused to take any action. He was already exceedingly unpopular, and the aldermen of Norwich decided that they had to make a stand. They obtained an order from the Speaker of the House of

Commons for the mayor to be removed from office and be taken to London, under the control of a messenger sent to Norwich for that purpose.

As soon as the order was received, the mayor's friends and allies drew up their own petition to Parliament, testifying to his good government and behaviour. The petition was put about the city and read in churches as a protest against his removal, and many hundreds signed it. The city's aldermen were incensed by this defiance of the instructions of Parliament; they knew that the petition was a muster roll of royalists, and they could see that trouble was brewing. The mayor's supporters began to assemble in the marketplace on Sunday evening, as a show of strength. This crowd threatened the London messenger and the sheriff, saying that they would 'Hang them upon the Castle Hill, upon Gardiner's mare, and ham-string anybody that should offer to carry Mr Mayor away'.

The mayor asked his supporters to disperse, to maintain peace in the city, but the crowd were getting stirred up, growing in number, and many were armed. The leaders of the crowd then asked that, at a shout given at eight the next morning, the crowd was to reassemble. It was late in the evening on the Sunday by the time my father returned home, deeply troubled, though he tried to reassure my mother that it would all come to nothing. Early the next morning, my father ordered my mother and all the children upstairs, to stay there until he returned. He called on two of his apprentices to protect his beloved family if the trouble should spread to our part of the city. He had faith in them for they were loyal and knew he would reward them well.

My father then left and joined his fellow aldermen, and on their approach to the Chapel-Field they heard a loud shout and a great number of men immediately assembled. They saw that the messenger from London was trying to escort the mayor away, but the strength of the crowd stopped him, and for his own safety he was quickly escorted out of the city by some men who would do him no harm, leaving the mayor behind. The mob was growing stronger and more determined and would not listen to reason. They continued to move through the city, breaking windows, plundering dwellings, helping themselves to all the victuals, wine and beer, and seizing arms.

The aldermen had sent word around the city warning people to stay off the streets and lock themselves in at home. The shopkeepers, with no trade and fearful of the riot, shut up and secured their shops. At about three o'clock, the crowd, now at least 2,000 strong, surged forward as one great violent mass. They went past the great church of St Peter Mancroft, seemingly without a thought of their conscience, to the Committee House, a building where the city's arms and ammunition were stored. A group of rioters broke in and the ringleaders began to throw all sorts out of the windows, a fire pan, a tapestry, a pair of tongs, a bridle and bundles of paper. The mob continued to ransack the armoury for there was no one to stop them and then they ran, carrying their deadly bounty, to the Chapel-Field, to arm themselves with muskets, pikes, swords, pistols and bandoliers.

Amongst the general confusion a man was heard shouting a warning, of gunpowder carelessly spilt on the stairs, but still men hurried away carrying their hats full of looted gunpowder out of the Committee Chamber. The powder ignited and no fewer than ninety-eight barrels of gunpowder went off at one crack, devastating the Committee House and the surrounding area. Many of the rioters were blown into the air, others threw down their arms and ran away. My father said it was impossible to describe the great force of that explosion. He had been some distance away at the time, but even so he had been knocked off his feet and quite deafened by the blast, somehow finding shelter as the debris rained down all around him. Later, a troop of soldiers arrived and took charge, overpowering the rioters at the Chapel-Field and chasing others down through the lanes and alleyways of our stunned city. My father had made his way home, passing others on the way, all completely deaf and deathly white from the dust.

He paused in his telling of this tale, and we all sat by the fire, safe and together, but not uttering a word as we waited for him to continue. He took another gulp of ale, then told of his relief at seeing that our house had withstood the blast. He glanced over our heads at my mother, who, that night, had shrieked upon seeing him, covered as he was in a terrible mixture of blood and dust, and then thrown herself at him, not caring about the deadly mess. Then she had cried, finally giving in to her fear after trying to calm her children all through that long dreadful day as she listened out for my father's footsteps. That night, as shouts still rang out in the distance, my mother and father gathered all their children onto their bed, restlessly dozing on and off, and me, oblivious and content, snug in amongst them all.

Early the next morning, after another sluice down with some buckets of water and in fresh clothes, my father had walked back to the city, past people who were still stumbling around in a daze unable to find their way home. He saw that the whole site had been destroyed, including the Committee House, Chapel-Field House and many surrounding dwellings. They stumbled over a many-coloured carpet of glass, laid down from the shattered stained windows of the mighty St Peter Mancroft and the church of St Stephen, where many of the dead were soon to be buried. We were later told that the violence of the shock itself had been felt throughout most of the county, and some unfortunate people had been maimed or killed, even at a great distance from the blowe, by the fall of the stones and timber.

In all, over 100 people were killed or wounded that dreadful day, soldiers and rioters, as well as innocent bystanders and citizens, killed as their homes collapsed around them. My father and others spent the next week grimly digging the corpses out of the timber and debris – some whole and recognisable, some not. They recovered the battered bodies of servants, blacksmiths, labourers, gunsmiths and a wool-comber, accompanied by the rising cries of their kin as they discovered the grisly fate of their loved ones. My father spoke no more of that terrible day, but as we crept out of the room at the end of his tale he turned from the fire and said, 'If God could grant me one wish, it would be that men, for it is usually men, in this city, our country, all over the world, would learn some sense.'

For my father, this was a darker tale even than his stories of the plague, for he lost many friends that dreadful day, and for the remainder of his life he was haunted by the deaths of the innocent children, their bodies crushed or torn apart by the explosion. I later heard, for of course he did not tell us this part, that the morning after, having cleared the debris and bodies for many hours, and sick with tiredness and stunned with disbelief, my father had found a tiny hand. He had continued to search, beyond exhaustion, but he could not find the body of that child. I heard, too, that he waylaid the frantic rector of the ruined St Peter Mancroft, amidst the digging of graves, and insisted that he bury that tragic little relic, unnamed and unmarked but remembered forever by my father.

HANGINGS IN DITCHES

As the dust settled upon the ground and bodies were buried and houses repaired, the city sought to understand what had caused such an appalling event. The violence of the mob, the sheer force of the explosion, the damaged buildings and the deaths of innocents, all served to subdue the people of Norwich. Some were ashamed that they had been swept up in the violence and destruction of that day and the city was calmer afterwards, for a while at least. The day after the riot, the mayor, of his own accord, rode to Parliament, whereupon he was fined and discharged from office.

Later that year, on Christmas Day, the justices of the city held their sessions, before whom 108 persons were prosecuted and fined, having been identified either as rioters or for receiving looted arms and goods. Eight men received the sentence of death and were executed, by hanging, in the Castle Ditches on 2nd January, at the same time as two old women, Margaret Turrell and Anne Dant, were put to death for witchcraft. For years afterwards, in the inns of Norwich, rumours were whispered regarding the whereabouts of the arms looted from the Committee House. Most were never traced despite a call for all arms to be brought to the City Hall; some were later sold in shady dealings in alleyways, others were hidden up chimneys, and some were passed down through families, a gruesome reminder of that most terrible of times.

A DESOLATE SITE

Remembering my father's sad story, as I stood with the rector and his wife at that place of destruction, I thought, too, of all the brutal events that had occurred throughout our country during the years of my childhood. How we seemed to be constantly at war, yet men and women struggled to provide for their families while our wealthy leaders squabbled, oblivious to the suffering of others. I realised that it was not surprising that the fate of the city's mad folk was of little concern to the ordinary people of Norwich, for they were merely trying to survive themselves. I prayed that by my work, when the Bethel finally stood, some would be enlightened and able to show more charity towards our tormented brethren. That people would not be so quick to blame lunacy on the wrath of God. I, at least, had hope.

I could see the rector and his wife looking at me as I stood, waiting patiently for me to speak, but I had hesitated. Did I really want to build my sanctuary, my place of peace, on that abandoned site, with its tragic history? I had not even considered premises or land in the centre of Norwich. I had ruled it out as being too expensive, and I had so wanted to build my Bethel in Thorpe, to stay close to Samuel. But I could see how it would be a perfect position, close to the market, large enough to create some private space, and even the garden I had so desired. And, as it had lain undeveloped for over half a century, I was hopeful it could be obtained at a good price, with sufficient money remaining to build the Bethel to my own designs. What better way would there be to eradicate the tragic memories of its past than to use that desolate site for such a godly purpose?

I had too many thoughts racing through my mind to be able to say much to my companions, so with a smile I simply thanked them, picked up my skirts and hurried back to the church of St Peter Mancroft, to pray under its great wooden roof. There, with its angels looking down upon me, I gave thanks to God for guiding me to that place and for reminding me of my faith. I was certain it was His will that I had Samuel's memory to keep me strong. And I knew I had finally found a suitable site for the Bethel. More than ever, I believed I could fulfil my promise.

WIDOWS ARE WILFUL AND WILL BE OBEYED

But, as I had come to learn, nothing is easy, and once again I ran into problems, mainly with securing the site. Many on the City Committee were reluctant to lease the land to a woman; well, to be clear, they just refused, with no room for discussion or appeal. I heard later that at least some of the aldermen had supported me, but unfortunately they were not able to persuade the men who made the final decision. I was not impressed, but I was determined that I would not be thwarted by those ridiculous men and their pretence at power. I called again on those who had known my father. I was not surprised to find that all his old friends were now dead, for time had passed, but some of my father's former apprentices and journeymen had become freemen and reached positions of influence themselves. A few showed me the door, unwilling to entertain the idea of a woman overseeing such a venture – the words 'Woman, be silent' ringing in my ears after one particularly dispiriting encounter. Some refused to help, perhaps remembering old political rivalries and jealousies, or even their family's allegiances during the Civil Wars – royalists against parliamentarians, all over again. Others, those who lived in the centre of the city, told me, quite forcefully, that they simply did not want a house full of lunaticks on their doorstep.

Still, I gathered enough support to resubmit my application for a lease. When the City Committee next met I attended the Guild Hall, though I was not allowed into the Chamber to hear their discussions. Eventually the men filed out, as I stood, hopeful. I noticed my unwelcome admirer, as odious as ever, looking at me, not with desire now but with triumph. A shake of the head from one of my supporters confirmed that they had been unable to persuade the committee to my cause and my application had once again been rejected. Feeling all their eyes upon me, I simply walked away, outwardly proud but repeating my father's words, over and over to myself, '*Per ardua stabilis, per ardua stabilis*, strength in adversity, Mary, stay strong.' And then, under my breath of course, but with a smile, 'Kiss my arse.'

Despite this setback I continued to be filled with energy and I revisited my plans each evening, fitting them to that derelict site and talking to anyone who would listen. I had set my heart on this and I was determined that I would be granted a lease, for I believed that God had guided me to that place. The executors of Samuel's will had assured me that the money from his legacy would be ready when I required it, and I arranged for outline plans for the building to be drawn up. I even had some new clothes made, neat and respectable and with no needless decoration or frills but befitting my status as a wealthy widow, for I had appearances to keep up now. I was ready, but I had longer still to wait, and, though I tried to occupy myself, time passed too slowly.

But widows are wilful, and they will be obeyed. Eventually the men who sat in control of the committee were replaced by some who were more sympathetic to my cause. More sympathetic, perhaps, because I had used my time wisely. I had called on their wives, to explain what I was planning and how it would benefit the good people of Norwich, and how the men who supported me would look most benevolent and wise. And perhaps the wives of those great men had a little influence themselves. Or perhaps I do the men an injustice; perhaps they had remembered my father and the support he had once given them and the debt they could now repay by helping his wilful daughter. For whatever reason, the committee agreed to consider my application once again. Looking back, the delay was probably time well spent for, over those months, as I talked and explained my ideas, I found four decent men who were willing to support me openly, and who had agreed to use their time and influence to help me. Without their belief in me and my vision for the Bethel, that desolate site might have remained simply a tragic part of our city's history, a dramatic tale to be repeated to later generations.

But this wilful widow was finally able to give thanks to God that, on the twelfth day of December 1712, at a meeting of the City Committee, a thousand-year lease was granted to those four men on my behalf, for that waste piece of ground, in the parish of St Peter Mancroft. It was designated that the land should be used 'for the building of a House or Houses for the benefit and use of such Persons as are Lunaticks'. It was virtually a gift. That it was leased by the city for a thousand years at a peppercorn rent perhaps also reflected the strength of the support I now had from the leaders of our city for my hospital, my sanctuary, for Samuel's Bethel.

I will forever be wholly grateful for the support of those four decent men: William Cockman, John Hall, John Morse and Timothy Greene. They were all men of stature within our city, and no doubt their influence did much to ease the way in my endeavours. Justice Cockman was the mayor of Norwich when my leased was granted and he was keen to continue to support me, not least because it strengthened his alliances with the other trustees, all powerful men. John Hall and John Morse were aldermen of the city and both had served as mayor. Mr Timothy Greene was a quite upstanding member of our community, known for his kindness and generosity.

Once the lease was agreed, we had another short wait while all the money from the sale and rent of the lands from Samuel's bequest was released. During that time, I had many meetings with Mr Morse, who was kindly and expertly advising me regarding the practicalities of building the Bethel. He had appointed an architect to draw up the final plans according to my detailed instructions. I was quite clear in my desire, as I upheld Samuel's wish, to ensure that the city's poor lunaticks would be able to feel they were in a private house, that they would have accommodation that was clean, comfortable and safe. I wanted surroundings that were a far cry from those found in the Bedlam, where, I had heard on very good authority, the lunaticks continued to live in dark, damp cells with only filthy straw as bedding. It did not take a great deal of sense to realise that such conditions would surely make even the sanest person quite distressed or even mad with despair. We could not expect our residents to improve and eventually be able to leave if they had to contend with such appalling surroundings. I was firm in my requirements. We would have individual sleeping rooms, bright communal areas for those who were improving and where I planned to have daily prayers, a vegetable garden for those who might be fit for such duties, and a rose garden for visitors to sit with their relatives and enjoy a few moments of normality.

I could feel that my dear Mr Morse was becoming quite exhausted, though he tried hard to be patient. He had begun to understand how important this was to me, for I had spent many hours, even years, planning this House so that it would meet with Samuel's approval. The architect seemed a little uncomfortable with all the demands of this wilful widow, though Mr Morse backed me every time there was a dispute. I think we were all relieved to hear at last that everything was in order and the building of the new hospital could finally begin. I had to curtail my excitement, though, for there was yet one more annoying delay. The plans had been approved but at the last moment it was noticed that the frontage of the House would be more than that of the land that we had leased, by about twelve feet. So much for exact specifications. In any case, we had to purchase a further piece of ground, to the west, for £300. But, eventually, everything was in place. Perhaps we were ready. Perhaps Samuel could rest a little easier.

Eight

'THE HOUSE I HAVE BUILT, I HAVE CALLED BETHEL'

This House was built for the benefit of distrest Lunaticks Ano Dom. 1713 and is not to be alienated or employed to any other use or purpose whatsoever

After all our conversations, I was pleased that Mr Morse and the architect had indeed listened very carefully and noted my exact requirements, and they had cleverly turned them into building specifications for the House. The drawings were so beautiful that I spent hours just looking at them, imagining the day when I could finally open the doors to the Bethel. It was to be a two-storey building with an attic and two wings, set back from the road. The front of the House faced Committee Street. At the back of the House, towards the Chapel-Field, I had my garden, laid out behind some secure walls, and there I planned to plant a tree, an apple tree, in memory of that poor soldier, shot for no good reason so many years ago. I felt that Samuel would do the same if he were alive.

The House would be completed in stages, and Mr Morse showed me the building agreement between himself and Richard Starling (the carpenter) and Edward Freeman (the mason). Mr Starling and Mr Freeman were paid ten shillings each as down payment, with the remainder to follow as the building progressed. Though my sight was too poor to read all of that great long document, it gave me confidence to have it all set out in such detail, from the width of the walls to the size of the nails.

Excerpts from:

Article of Agreement indented, made, concluded and agreed upon this seventh day of March in the eleventh year of the reigne of Our Sovereigne Lady Ann by the Grace of God of Great Britaine, France and Ireland, Queen, Defender of the Faith and in the year of Our Lord one thousand seven hundred and twelve.

By 15th day of April 1713

The House from East to West within the walls to be eighty-nine feet and a half in length, with two wings twenty and seven feet in length each, joyned to the building.

Shall make two cellars, one in the south-east corner and the other in the south-west corner of the building, fifteen feet square and six feet high, and set windows in the cellars of five inches by four inches. The windows to be glazed with quarrell glasse.

The foundations of the house shall be eighteen inches deep and eighteen inches broad, with good mortar and stones or brick to the level of the ground. The walls of the house shall be built with good mortar and dry hard burnt or crimson brick up to the water table.

Shall divide the first floor into three rooms either side of a central passageway, which shall be from the doore in the middle of the fore front to the doore in the middle of the back front.

Shall lay and place a good floor.

Shall make and place all the doores and windows of the first floor.

By 15th day of June 1713

Shall make and place the second floor. Make all windows of the second floor and set in place at the front and back of the house.

By 15th day of August 1713

Add the third floor, add the rafters and larth of the roof with good hard larth such as are usually sold at two shillings and sixpence a bunch and nayle them down to every rafter at a seven-inch gage with good fourpenny nayles and cover all the said roof and building with good English tile made with good mortar.

Erect and build up all the four stacks of chimbleys with good mortar and bricks and finish and top or head all of the chimbleys.

Shall divide the second floor into rooms as on the first floor, three rooms on either side of the passage in the middle of the house, and a room over the passage. And make partitions four inches thick with studs and brick, in these rooms.

Shall and will hang all and every of the said doores with good strong home-made double-jointed gimmers made a foot and a half long on the side of the jointe the one way and the width of the doore the other way, put on and rivited with clynkers.

Shall make and erect a staircase from the bottom of each cellar up to the second floor AND shall and will make the covers and stands of the same of good dry redd wood with deals and the strings and bearers of the said staircases of good oake.

Shall seal and plaster with good haire morter under every floor joyce, under the staircase. Shall plaster with good hard morter all the walls and the stud and brick partitions.

Pave the passage in the middle of the said house and all the rooms on the first floor with good white pavements. And the floors in both the said cellars with good red pavements.

And make a two-light window over every outward doorway.

AND make, build, erect and do everything about the said house substantially and in workmanlike manner... in such manner and proportion and according to the said plann.

AND shall and will make all the wood works used in and about the said house of good oake timber, or other wood as herein before mentioned and shall not or will not use any timber that have any sapp or is any way decayed where it shall or may be any way prejudishall or hurtfull to the said building.

AND shall and will finish and adorne all things in the rooms... in the manner as houses are usually finished and adorned.

AND shall and will erect, make, build and finish all the said house and the rooms within the same and leave the same by the sneck on or before the nine and twentieth day of September now next ensuing 1713.

I travelled into Norwich as often as I could, on days when Ellen was calm enough to be left for a few hours, and I watched as the very foundations were dug. I used my handkerchief to flick the dried mud off a low wall, and I settled myself there, directly opposite where the door to my House would be. Quite fascinated, I marvelled at the skill of the mason and the carpenter, amazed at how the House could take shape so quickly. Sometimes I was accompanied by Hannah, my dear friend, who shared my excitement and listened endlessly to my prattling on, and even Ellen, on occasion, came with us. Together we sat, in a line, on our wall, impervious to the smirks of the less charitable, but still curious, passers-by.

I watched the men as they cheerfully toiled, some digging deep into the earth while others carried the bricks and timber onto the site. After a while I realised that my presence was perhaps a little irritating, though the men at least made an effort to moderate their occasionally quite foul language. I felt I had to mention their louder oaths to Mr Morse and suggested that he should warn them to be more careful. There were still those who might report them for blasphemy. I do not like to hear any person invoking God's name in such a way, but I can understand that it may occasionally happen. Indeed, I observed one man cry out, as a heavy timber fell and broke his toes, and under such circumstances I forgave him his lapse. Sadly, according to our laws, the courts could have been upon him, and I had heard of the most horrific punishment for those found guilty. One of my father's grimmer tales told of a man, spitefully accused of blasphemy by a neighbour, who had the letter 'B' branded upon his forehead, and I would not wish that upon any person, let alone one who had a hand in the building of my hospital. To my mind those archaic laws were merely another means of controlling the common person, who should be at liberty to speak her, or his, mind, but I fear we are still a long way away from that kind of freedom. It appeared that Mr Morse did indeed have a quiet word with the men, for they started to greet me with a polite 'Good-day'. Perhaps he had also informed them of who I was and what the House meant to me, so they need no longer wonder about the decrepit widow who turned up and settled down to watch them so intently.

When the site was prepared, and the building had begun, Mr Morse strode over one day, and invited me to lay the foundation stone. Holding onto his arm, I hobbled across the road, picking my way carefully between the debris that covered the ground. The foundation stone was already in place and I spread a trowel of mortar on its surface, then stood back and started to say a few words. But, though I had been preparing a short speech for weeks, I faltered, as the enormity of it all struck me, and I stood in silence, as Mr Morse waited patiently. After several minutes, he took my arm again and gently guided me back to my wall, where I looked up at him and, with a nod, I smiled and said, 'Yes, Mr Morse, thank you… it is all coming along nicely.'

I would not be allowed to enter the House for many months, and after a while I restricted myself to weekly visits, when I would meet with Mr Morse, Mr Freeman and Mr Starling, and they would take time to explain their progress. They usually showed me some of the fixtures, the snecks and gimmers, even the great nails, so that I could hold them and feel part of the House as it was formed.

After each and every one of my visits to the site I gave thanks to God, in the church of St Peter Mancroft, in the quiet area near to the Resurrection tapestry. I had prayed in there so many times that I knew all of that great tapestry in detail – the section that shows Christ appearing to Mary Magdalene as a gardener still makes me smile, though I rather think it alludes to His ability to nurture us so that we can flourish, rather than to any fondness for digging. The depiction of my Lord holding a spade always inspired me, and as I made my way home I formed an idea of how the garden at the Bethel could be used more fully. I decided to divide the grounds into sections. We would have one area of tranquillity with plain planting, just greens and whites, surrounded by small trees, or perhaps a willow tree, for those whose senses needed calming. Then another area filled with more colour and scent, for those whose senses needed stimulating. I planned a separate garden near to the House, surrounded by a low wooden fence, and filled with roses, as many rosa mundi as I could find. Finally, space for my physick garden and a large area for growing our own vegetables. I spent several happy nights redesigning and redrawing my plans for the garden, until, at last, I was sure they were quite perfect.

In May, I visited Samuel's grave and, instead of my usual sad reminiscences, I told him, talking very quietly so that no one would overhear and decide I had lost my senses, of how I could see his Bethel rising from that forsaken piece of waste ground. As I left I took from my pocket one of the nails I had been given by Mr Freeman, along with a small trowel I had acquired from the site. Kneeling, I buried that nail from the Bethel in the soft ground by the door of Samuel's church before patting the earth softly back into place.

'WITH SUCH SACRIFICES GOD IS WELL PLEASED'

As the days passed and I sat on my wall watching the Bethel take shape, I was approached by many passers-by. Some were merely curious about the new building which was to fill the space that had existed for more than half a century. Many were pleased to listen to my plans for a sanctuary for the disturbed – one I proposed would be open to all, not just to those who were wealthy enough to pay for a room. I was joined, at times, by the rector, who strolled up from his church at St Peter Mancroft to sit with me, and his wife, who often brought some bread or fruit to sustain me during my vigil.

I also became used to hearing the vile comments from some of the less charitable in our city, who were not pleased to hear of the new 'madhouse', and who went out of their way to tell me so. They mostly shouted at me as they passed by, but some would loom over me as they shared their views on the sins of the mad, invariably when I was sitting alone. I was not particularly concerned at their behaviour as I knew that Mr Morse's men would be watching from the Bethel. They would soon come over, shovels in hand, to protect their defenceless widow if any of those angry and misguided folk should threaten my person. I simply waited for my detractors to pause in their ranting, so I could offer them a share of my dinner, while I explained my intentions, and tried to persuade them to be more charitable. In the face of such vehement opposition, which in truth I had not fully expected, once again I remembered my father's words, *Per ardua stabilis*. I continued to sit, boldly, on my wall, to stand up to those who were against me and the building that was rising, defiantly, in front of their eyes.

Over that summer, much work was achieved and finally I was allowed to go inside the House. I could see the staircases of good oak which had been installed on either side of the central passageway. The floors were all paved (white in the wings of the House and red in the cellars), and the windows were glazed with good clear glass. Shutters had been added to the windows and these were being painted for a second time with good white lead and oil. As we walked around I kept mostly silent, accompanied by a slightly anxious Mr Morse, who noted my suggestions for small improvements. I could see the Bethel clearly now and I began to imagine it filled with those in need of peace. I decided it would be prudent to build a straw-house, for I was certain that we would need a supply of fresh dry straw for the worst of our lunaticks. I was cross with myself, after all my years of planning, that I had not thought of this before, but the ever-patient Mr Morse merely agreed, and said he would talk to Mr Freeman.

It was a beautifully constructed building, with wide corridors and a lovely fresh smell, but, as we made our way into the rooms that were to accommodate the lunaticks, some details reminded us of its ultimate purpose. The doors of each of the rooms for the lunaticks were cut with a hole, six inches square at a convenient height, and fitted with an iron grate on the inside and a shutter on the outside. The windows were fitted with three-inch iron bars in case any of the lunaticks, during their moments of greatest despair, should be tempted to jump out. Despite these grim reminders, I also hoped that at least some of them might find solace in the pleasant view through their windows, though as I peered out I could see that the grounds of the House were still overgrown and covered with piles of rubble and earth. Mr Morse quickly assured me that the area would be cleared by the time of my next visit, and that I would be able to see the gardens emerging from the mess. I produced my final plans for the outline of the garden, which now required low walls and paths to divide it into sections. He suppressed a sigh but, with admirable grace, said that he would endeavour to have the work carried out. I gave him my approval for all his labours and thanked him for his careful consideration to detail as we walked along the passageway and out of the front door.

There, Mr Morse showed me the recently installed oil lamps, set on the outside of the Bethel and towards the street, for the convenience of passers-by. They would be lit as it grew dark, and would remain alight until eleven o'clock at night, from Michaelmas to Lady Day. I was heartened that the Bethel's lamps would shine out, so that all around could see this great building. We would be able to show the people of Norwich and the visitors to our great city that lunaticks need not be hidden away or kept in loathsome conditions. And in that way, perhaps, we could show people that the poor disturbed souls within our city need not be feared. Perhaps we could persuade them to show more Christian charity to those who suffer so. As Samuel had wished.

BY THE SNECK

More months passed. The days were getting shorter, and the leaves were turning, but finally it was done. The House was complete, and Samuel's Bethel stood, proud amongst the crumbling buildings around it. I was content but also quite exhausted. I felt as though I had been holding my breath for years, waiting for this moment, and I let out a gentle sigh of relief, for now at least, as there was much work still to be done before we could admit our first lunaticks. Yet, as I made my final walk around the whole building with Mr Morse, I was satisfied that all was as we had detailed in the building agreement. I thanked him, from my heart, for his monumental efforts in creating my House, and a huge smile filled his weary face. For the first time in months, there was silence. The mason and carpenter and their men had left for now, though some would return to finish the high wall around the outside of the House and garden, to keep us secure.

I asked Mr Morse to grant me a few moments in the garden, which had been cleared according to my instructions and prepared for planting. I walked, alone, in the area I intended to be the quiet garden, like the one in the Resurrection tapestry. It was evening, the city itself was peaceful, and I could smell the freshly turned earth. I was reminded of the long years before I had met Samuel, when I was caring for those in my family afflicted with lunacy. I recalled also my faith in God's grace in blessing me with the use of my reason and understanding, and later, my determination to create this place of hope. I paused, and then I looked to the sky and spoke out loud:

'As a monument of my thankfulness for this invaluable mercy,
I set little Bethel for that purpose.'

I walked back, bid farewell to Mr Morse, then made my way along Committee Street to the church, to give my usual prayers, which were longer on that momentous day, for I had much to thank Him for. I left the church just as the great bells began to ring, and I paused and turned around to look once again at my wondrous House. The Bethel filled the space that had existed for so long after the Great Blowe, and the wasteland that had surrounded it had been tamed into my neat garden. How I so wished that my father could have stood beside me and seen that something so good had been built on that once forsaken site.

As the sun slowly descended, I could just see the roof tiles on the front of the House. Below them, deeply engraved in large letters in the stone above the door, were the words taken from Hebrews, the thirteenth chapter and sixteenth verse. I had instructed that there would be no other inscription, and as the letters wore out they would be renewed, to remain visible to all who came to our door and to those who passed by, for all time:

BETHEL

TO DO GOOD AND TO SHARE WITH OTHERS FORGET NOT,
FOR WITH SUCH SACRIFICES GOD IS WELL PLEASED

It was 1713 and the Bethel stood. I had fulfilled Samuel's wish and I was at peace.

Nine

'MY WORTHY AND FAITHFUL FRIENDS'

I was sixty-six years old when, at last, I moved into a room at the Bethel – the very room I now sit in, looking out over the garden at the back of the House, as I tell my story. I had been unsure about leaving Thorpe, where I had spent so many happy years with Samuel, but I was certain, in some way, I could feel close to him here too for I know this House was very much in his heart even if he did not survive to see its creation. I still have his boots, polished and set in place by the fire grate. The books I chose from his study, fill the shelves on the wall facing my bed. The engraving of my Lord in its silver frame, the gift from my father when I was a young girl, sits on my side table, next to our two books – my John Donne and Samuel's John Bunyan. My room has barely changed since I first moved here, and I still need little else to comfort me.

Ellen insisted on the room adjoining mine and we kept our doors open while she became accustomed to our new home, though she ventured a little further from me each day, and I was thankful that she appeared content. We shared the House with a small number of people who would help to run the Bethel when the lunaticks started to arrive. My first appointment was a cook, as I was determined that our lunaticks would have wholesome fare to help in their recovery. I had in mind a woman from a family I knew when Samuel was alive, recently widowed and in search of lodgings. I approached Mrs Crick, who kindly agreed to give us a trial, though she was, she said, a little wary of working in a 'madhouse'. Gently, I explained that I considered this place to be a hospital, for those with an illness of their mind, as I abhor the name 'madhouse' and will not have it used here. I'm not sure it completely reassured her, though I could hear her singing as she clattered around, getting used to the kitchen. She would have her own kitchen maids to assist her when we had more residents, but, at first, she insisted she could manage on her own. We also had a few orderlies who cleaned the House from top to bottom, for, whilst the carpenter had moved on, his dust had not. We had two maids, for general duties, and they seemed happy with their spacious, warm and dry rooms up on the top floor, though perhaps they would have preferred not to be under the ever-watchful eye of Mrs Crick.

I also employed Edward Brightwell, to tend the garden. He worked for my father and though he was quite elderly I felt that he shared my vision for a little sanctuary within this sanctuary. I was pleased that he remembered my father, too, for there were few still alive that knew him well. On occasion Mr Brightwell would share a memory with me, some tale of my father that I had not heard before. I learnt of the families that my father had helped when they were in need, and of the children who attended school or gained apprenticeships because of a recommendation from him – all this done quietly, and with no want of recognition. Sometimes, mid-way through a complicated, rambling tale, Mr Brightwell would pause when he realised he should not elaborate further, for his story included details about my father's more raucous visits to the Angel. I pretended not to notice when his words faded away, for I was grateful for his reticence.

Mr Freeman, and his men, returned to complete the high wall around the Bethel House and gardens, and Mr Brightwell followed along after them, patiently repairing the damage they caused to his neat flower beds with their great boots. He worked in the garden for long hours, keen, like all of us, to get everything ready. I told him he must not over-tire himself, but when I saw him struggle to dig the hole for the soldier's apple tree, I hurried out to suggest that he should appoint some trustworthy men to help him with the digging and the harder tasks – in view of his age, I thought, though I did not say that out loud. Mr Brightwell appeared relieved and said he would ask at the marketplace the next day, for there were many who were grateful for the chance of a day's work for a few pennies. He was clearly very pleased to move here from his draughty room above a quite disreputable ale house which backed onto the castle ditches. He said he liked the peace, and that for the first time in many years he felt safe within our walls. He seemed not to mind the bars on the windows, or the iron grate and shutter on the door.

We still had much to do before we could admit our first residents, but we had made a start. I organised the rooms of this House such that we could accommodate twelve lunatics, though we made space for more, when we needed to. The layout of the House is still very much as it was in those early days: the lunaticks' sleeping rooms in the west wing, reached by one of the staircases, the rooms for the attendants above, so that there is help nearby at all times, and there are two cellars, for our more disturbed or violent lunaticks. Mrs Crick's kitchen is on the ground floor, with an adjoining room where the attendants and maids take their breaks and meals, and next to that is the dining room for the lunaticks. On the other side of the central passageway, in the east wing, is a large, communal day room for the lunaticks, then the bath-house and laundry. On the next floor, Ellen and I have our rooms, accessible by our own staircase. Above us, in the attic, is the accommodation for the house maids, Mrs Crick and her kitchen assistants. As time went on and demand for our care increased, we added partitions to the sleeping rooms so that we could admit more of those in need.

We had the furniture for some of the rooms at least, quite plain but sturdy, and newly made by Mr Starling and his apprentices.

More pieces turned up each week and the rooms for the lunaticks began to take shape. Mr Starling also arranged for four benches to be positioned around the garden, with one for the rose garden. I asked that they be made in the style of the old bench that Samuel and I had in our little paradise at the rectory, and Mr Starling painstakingly carved each one with the flowers we had growing there – roses, cornflowers, foxgloves and columbine. I was becoming more sentimental as I aged and took comfort in making small changes here and there so that those I had lost would, in some way, be part of this place. I put a few of my mother's pots and odd bits of her crockery in the kitchen, all very old, but I thought perhaps they could be of some use.

I asked Mrs Crick to inform me of her requirements for her kitchen and noted that we still needed plates and bowls and spoons for the lunaticks. I was concerned about how we might clothe our more destitute residents, but then I heard that my friend, the rector of St Peter Mancroft, had asked his congregation to support us. We had many people from the parish turn up at our door, perhaps curious to see inside but also bearing kind donations of clothes, shawls, and old, but serviceable, shoes and boots. Our lunaticks would be the warmest and best dressed around, of that I was sure. Even some of the poorer inhabitants of this city, who had little to give, turned up with an offering: some vegetables they had grown themselves, a jug of their home-brewed ale, or some sticks for our fires. I was overwhelmed by their generosity and I made sure to greet people and thank them in person for their kindness. I also directed those who appeared to be in want themselves to Mrs Crick's kitchen for some of the pottage she had brewing constantly, before they went on their way.

Mr Brightwell had quite a collection of plant cuttings and shrubs donated from the gardens of some of our wealthy friends, and there was even a small rose bush simply left on our doorstep. I had planned the garden in detail, not only the different sections but also the plants it would contain, but I found room for the generous gifts from those who wished us well. Thankfully I had the foresight to bring some seeds and plants from my physick garden in Thorpe, and once again, for the final time, I hoped, I recreated it. I was sure that such herbs and flowers and roots would prove essential when we had lunaticks here in need of soothing tisanes or warming tonics. It was also another reminder of Samuel, for once upon a time he had tended many of the plants that produced those very seeds. I liked that feeling, knowing that life would endure, long after we were gone. Sadly, though, the rosa mundi did not take well to being moved, and I had to purchase more for the rose garden in front of the lunaticks' day room. They were an extravagance, yet it brought me pleasure to imagine the sweet scent that would come from the following summer's blooms, and I hoped that others would delight in their perfume and beauty too.

Ellen kept herself busy, though I could see that she was slowing down a little. I had thought she might be upset at all the comings and goings, but she watched the daily deliveries from a distance and then took charge of sorting out each room as soon as the delivery men had left. She was still wary of people she did not know, but had become used to Mr Brightwell, and I often saw her wandering around the garden when he was there, pulling up a few stray weeds that he had missed, free for a while from her worries and ailments. She rarely left the Bethel, but perhaps the freedom she had, to be herself within our walls, also helped to reduce her anxieties. She once said she did not feel watched or judged here, for everyone knew her and paid her no attention and I was grateful for people's kindness towards her. I hoped and prayed that she would find some lasting peace. She still insisted that she must know where I was at all times, but, as long as she could find me if she started to feel uncertain, she was content.

Hannah called on us whenever she was in Norwich, and as we sat and chatted we always reminded Ellen of her raid on the rectory garden and she would come to life for a while and laugh along with us, saying it was one of her best memories. I heard her telling the story to Mr Brightwell; she repeated it often and, bless his kind heart, he always replied that they would be sure to take extra care of her precious plants. I heard him calling her his little 'Norfolk Dumpling', noticing perhaps that she had become quite plump – for the calmness of her mind and Mrs Crick's good food had helped her to gain a little weight. I thought to reprimand him, but I believe it was affectionately meant, so I let it pass.

It was helpful that Ellen could keep herself occupied as I still had much to do. There were always people to organise, there was the linen to be purchased for the sleeping rooms, and we needed all sorts of tools and implements for the fire grates and such like. I retired to my room each evening quite exhausted but pleased with my endeavours. Yet, however much progress we made, the list of all that I needed to do and the items we still required seemed to grow day by day.

I gave thanks to God that I could see the Bethel taking shape and what a wonderful place I knew it would be, but, nevertheless, I had to admit that I was tired. Late one afternoon, as I struggled around our garden to check the damage caused by a violent wind as it passed through the city, I saw that all the blossom from our apple tree had fallen and now covered the ground. Hurrying inside, I continued to shiver, feeling chilled to the very bone, and sat for a while, quite alone, in front of the fire in the day room, absorbing its warmth. I still missed Sam's energy and faithful support, but I was hopeful that there would soon be lunaticks in the day room, and I looked forward to the day when my hospital finally opened. I intended it to be a place where people were not fearful of entering, where they would know that they would be treated kindly. Despite my aches, my poor eyesight and my sadness at my losses, I had survived this long, and I would survive longer.

I had hope that God would grant us quieter times ahead. We had, with much pomp and great joy, proclaimed peace between Great Britain and France, and then with Spain. I prayed that it would last. And I thanked the Lord that we were free of smallpox as the last time it had raged through the city it had carried off a great number of people and devastated many families. My memories are long, and, of course, all that deadly pestilence was some years before and I was heartened to notice babies being born and families gradually rebuilding themselves. So, though I was filled with a tiredness I could not shake, I knew that we had much to be thankful for, and once the dreadful weather improved I was sure, if God willed it, I would find the strength to fulfil my promise to Samuel and open our doors.

Despite my fatigue, I loved to see the bustle all around me as we prepared for the lunatics. I was told to sit and rest, which I did, though I couldn't help but interfere a little for I knew exactly how things should be. It was an exciting time; I had loyal and good people with me at the Bethel and many friends in Norwich who supported me.

One of the first visitors to my House was my kind and generous friend, John Lougher. I remember my father mentioning his name as a worthy citizen of unshakeable integrity, and it was well known that he acquitted himself well to his own family in both economic and religious matters – he has certainly proved himself to be one of my most faithful and indefatigable friends. He was already a patron of many causes for the needy and industrious poor and I tried not to take up too much of his time, for I knew he could do much good elsewhere in this city. However, he promised that he would become involved in the Bethel if I ever had need, and I had faith that he would keep his word.

My days were also brightened by the regular visits of my other worthy and faithful friends, John Hall and William Cockman, who had supported my attempts to obtain the lease of the 'piece of waste ground' upon which the Bethel now stands. I call on these loyal men still to guide me and I continue to be grateful for their influence amongst the powerful – I certainly noticed there was less open opposition to my hospital when their involvement became more widely known. They also had an energy I was lacking, and they would always endeavour to procure some of the items on my list, when I asked. And though, for a time, I felt too unwell to leave this House, I was entertained by the news they brought when they called on me.

My most frequent visitor in the early days was John Hall. He had been guided and supported by my father, and had gone on to achieve even more power than my father once had. He had already stood as mayor, in 1701, and, though he was considered by some to be too young, they could not argue with his popularity. John Hall still lives nearby, at St George Tombland, and he regularly strolls through the streets to visit us. He may appear a little too full of his own importance, but I rather think he deserves to feel proud as he has done much good for the people of Norwich. When he visits me here we talk of life and politics and of our developing laws and the expansion of our great city. I can see he relaxes a little as he sits with me, no longer needing to portray his public self. He knows I am not impressed by any show of importance, and I sometimes think that he comes here for a little peace, for time away from his rowdy family and his demanding wife. And if he is surprised to talk on equal terms with a woman who is keen to voice her own opinions, then he is polite enough not to comment upon it – he must be used to me by now.

John Hall does not bother to tell tales or gossip, as he has learnt that I have little patience for such things. When I was unwell, he used to bring me a copy of the newspaper, not the *Norwich Post*, but another one, and I let him read a little of it for I was not able to concentrate for long myself. Thus, I heard of the 'Guardians of the City' and their endeavours in taking care of the poor. The guardians included many of the great and the good: the mayor, sheriffs and aldermen, and, of course, Mr Hall. Thirty-two other persons (eight from each of the city wards) were also chosen from the most honest, discreet and charitable inhabitants, by elections on the third day of May each year. This committee of men (and it was solely men, though I know many capable women who would be just as effective, given the chance) was tasked with ensuring the poor were provided for. With admirable efficiency, workhouses were built – one at the New Hall and another in the remains of the Duke's Palace. There was a growing understanding of our poorest inhabitants, many of whom were destitute through no fault of their own; perhaps they lacked caring families or had suffered ill health or ill fortune. The workhouses provided shelter for the needy, and they also encouraged the lazy, feckless and criminal inhabitants of our city to reform and to contribute to our society. I could see that the establishment of these workhouses would be of benefit to the Bethel, as we would only have to take those persons genuinely suffering from a loss of their senses. Thankfully we would not be required to provide shelter and care for the destitute poor, as this was never my intention, and their numbers would certainly overwhelm my modest hospital, leaving little space for my lunaticks.

I have always been proud that Norwich is renowned as a city where those who have experienced good fortune in their lives are generous in the support of the less fortunate. Despite all the talk of the achievements of the great and the good, I believe that generosity of spirit is the one true measure of a person's worth. According to Mr Hall, there are few other places in England whose inhabitants do as much for the poor as Norwich. I remember that, in my father's time, and even before, the people of our city had a fine tradition of charitable giving, without which many of our public institutions would not exist. Our Children's Hospital, for those unfortunates without parents to care for them, was built long ago, back in 1620. It was established by means of an endowment from Thomas Anguish, and has continued with the generous support of the people of Norwich. There is also Doughty's Hospital, which accommodates twenty-four men and eight women, in a house and gardens, though it does not have the means to care for any lunaticks.

Once it was built, our hospital was fairly well received amongst the people of Norwich, although, sadly, there were still those who lacked compassion. Even now, Mr Brightwell has to collect all sorts of rubbish thrown over our wall by people who seemingly can think of no other way to show their disapproval.

I had spent some of Samuel's legacy on building the Bethel, and on the furnishings and such like. Mr Morse had informed me that the final cost of the House itself was £414 2s 6d. It was my husband's desire that we should offer solace especially to the poorest lunaticks who had nowhere else to go and no means to pay for their care, and that was how I intended to use the remainder of his legacy. I continued to receive a substantial income from the rent of the lands and farms that I inherited from Samuel and I could pay for the ongoing costs of running the Bethel, but I had to be careful. Thus, I was heartened, and a little surprised, to receive many generous donations from the kind people of Norwich. Although, maybe I shouldn't have been surprised for Samuel had left £200 to each of the Norwich Hospitals in his will, and perhaps people remembered this and sought to repay his benevolence by supporting the Bethel, in his memory.

We had worked hard and my House was finally ready to admit its first residents, but I had become a little apprehensive about opening its doors. My health had continued to suffer during another bitterly cold winter, and I was confined to bed for many weeks, only able to manage small sips of Mrs Crick's warming pease-soup. Gradually, I recovered enough to potter about again, but I was weakened, and often had a little doze in the afternoons, which was quite unlike me. It took me several minutes to climb the stairs to my room, as I needed to pause on the way, whereas before I had skipped up, despite my age. Even as spring turned to summer, I continued to be plagued by a dreadful cough. In truth, I was also concerned about being overwhelmed by those requesting our help and of being unable to wholly provide the care they needed. However, I felt compelled, out of Christian charity, to accept a few poor souls to live under our roof before I was fully prepared. These first residents were admitted as an absolute necessity, for there was nowhere else for them to go, and I really could not contemplate turning them away. I have recorded some of the stories of the first lunaticks of the Bethel, though their details have been obscured as a precaution, for fear they might be recognised.

FAITH, OUR FIRST RESIDENT

One of the first (I shall call her Faith) was the daughter of a friend of my brother. Faith was a rather delicate young girl, about eighteen years old, who had rejected her parents' attempts to match her with a man they deemed suitable as a husband. When I received her letter asking if she could visit me, I had roused myself from my lethargy and was looking forward to seeing her and hearing the news of her family. I had not seen Faith for some time, and I remembered that she had always been delicate, but her appearance shocked me into silence – pale, feather-light and frail, skeletal. She was still a pretty girl, but I could see her blackened teeth, and I already suspected that she had been purging herself for I knew her family could easily afford the powders we used to keep our teeth clean. Faith was shivering, as if with cold, despite the warmth of the late summer sunshine, and I immediately sat her down. I gently put my shawl around her shoulders, the deep green and canary gold threads of the cloth clashing against the sallow of her skin, making her look quite unworldly. I called for Mrs Crick to bring a dish of my lemon balm tisane, the comforting remedy I used myself when I was feeling a particular lack of warmth. She had also noticed Faith's thin frame and kindly brought some of her freshly baked biscuits to try and tempt her.

After struggling through the usual polite inquiries, I deliberately left a break in the conversation and, almost immediately, Faith pleaded for my help. The sorry tale was that Faith had been suffering a great abhorrence to any sort of sustenance and was finding it more and more difficult to eat. I could see for myself how she struggled, for, though she drank all of her tisane, she could not even bear to put one of the biscuits into her mouth. She told of how she had become thinner and thinner and was constantly cold and lacking vitality. Though she described her attempts to eat at least some of her meals, when I gently questioned her she admitted that she could only pick at the food placed before her, and this had aroused her parents' concerns. Faith's request to see me had been precipitated by overhearing her parents talk of having her admitted to a private hospital for treatment. The hospital they favoured was run by a physician who charged quite exorbitant fees and had limited experience in the care of the tormented – he was, nonetheless, adept at charming the relatives of patients, while the poor unfortunates at his mercy suffered the most barbaric of so-called treatments, restraint and especially whippings. I had even heard stories of girls being held down whilst milk was poured down their throats. Faith had heard, too, and feared she would not survive. It was quite heartbreaking to hear her plead to be allowed to come and live at the Bethel. She wanted to get well, she said, and would stay only until she could learn how to eat again.

As we sat and talked, I recalled my father's stories of the sights he had seen in the shows at the Angel Inn, and how I had been troubled by my own, vivid image of the so-called living skeleton, unable to comprehend how such a thing could exist. I tried, as always, to hold true to my faith and my belief that God would not create such suffering, eventually choosing to believe that my father must have been exaggerating. However, in my time at the Bethel, I came to know of many such young people, often in great turmoil, who seemed to be made only of bones, and who somehow survived, on next to nothing to eat.

With thoughts, too, of my own dear sister, who would have been at the world's mercy without me to care for her, I was unable to refuse Faith's request for help. I sent a letter to her parents asking them to visit me. They attended and professed their concern for their daughter, and, though Faith sat through our discussions looking terrified that they might try and take her away, they readily agreed to let her come and stay with me. They refused to see her as a patient in need of treatment; rather, that I had taken her on as my companion. So, if that's what they told their friends, I could see no harm in letting them believe it, if it meant that Faith could gain the peace she needed. I called on the advice of a kindly medic, an old friend from Suffolk who was not known to Faith's family, or their friends. He had seen similar cases, he told me, many of whom did not recover but who simply starved themselves until they were too weak to lift a morsel of food to their mouths. Despite this rather grim prospect, we sat and discussed a possible treatment for Faith. We decided that she should be given time to rest, then later she could have some light duties, and he prescribed a course of physick which I immediately ordered from the apothecary. I would have liked her to have a daily drink of whey, which I planned to give to our lunatics, particularly those with melancholia, for I had read of its recuperative properties, but she refused. I insisted instead that Faith always sat with Ellen and me to eat and she agreed. I made no comment when she ate the tiniest of portions, though I was sorely tempted. I cannot explain how she was able to go about her daily routine, given the modicum of nourishment she existed on. Despite this, she cared for herself, was always neat and clean, and assisted me where she could, tidied my room, folded my clothes and accompanied me on my regular walks around our garden, even laughing as I stooped to move a precious frog into our vegetable beds. She seemed happier, calmer, almost content, but sometimes I heard her purge herself secretly after our meals.

The first few months passed. Faith gained more confidence and started to consume a little more, here and there. Outwardly, she even appeared 'cured', but she vehemently rejected any talk of returning home. I was able to reassure her that she would not be required to leave until she was ready, and that I approved of the constant efforts she was making to keep herself well. Her parents appeared to have forgotten her, but, though they never visited, they did pay regularly towards her keep. This arrangement seemed to suit Faith, who showed no desire to see them either. By the time I had accepted two more cases into my care, Faith had become a permanent resident at the Bethel. I felt, then, that I should consider her one of my failures; after all, I had intended this to be a place of cure and for facilitating a return home. Faith insisted that she was indeed better, but that she feared she would resume her old habits if she was made to leave. I was content to let her stay, for she had rather made herself indispensable to me given that my own health was deteriorating. Faith remained at the Bethel for many years, free to leave but choosing to stay – always very thin, but apparently eating just enough to remain well.

During Faith's first summer at the Bethel, Queen Anne died, and the country welcomed a new monarch, the seventh of my lifetime, King George the First. The gracious and pious Queen Anne had died at seven o'clock in the morning on the first day of August, in the fiftieth year of her age, and the thirteenth year of her reign, '… to the great sorrow of all her good subjects', or so it was reported in the newspapers. I noted her passing with particular sadness, for it was her courage and determination that had caused me to rediscover my own strength, and had led, ultimately, to the creation of the Bethel. Throughout her life, Queen Anne did her duty, but there was a little phrase that was being repeated, rather cruelly, I felt, after her death:

To save her country, twice she try'd.
First she fought and then she dy'd

I would not hear of it; she was a most conscientious person and a devout Christian. People did not know of all the good she did, even establishing a trust for the benefit of the poorer clergy. She also did much to unite our kingdom and I was sad and angry that she was being ridiculed. I hope history is kinder in its recording of her, and of her 'English heart'.

EPITAPH

The next distressed person to be given refuge at the Bethel was memorable simply for his sheer aura of loneliness, for he had apparently lived his whole life without any person to care for him at all. Known only as Bob, this man wandered the county, appearing in Norwich once a year or so, though never staying long before moving on. He was always alone, seeming to prefer his own company. He was of a clean appearance and, as he usually caused little trouble, he was quite well tolerated by the market stall holders, who did not mind when the occasional hot pie or herring went missing as he passed by. It had been noticed, though, that Bob had become quite odd in his manner, and one evening he had approached a group of soldiers, becoming most offensive and abusive. The soldiers had taken him to the county gaol, where the gaolers refused to have him as they argued that he had committed no crime. One of the soldiers had heard of the Bethel and conveyed him thence to our door. I could see that this vagrant was quite deranged in his manner, and I was fearful that if we turned him away the soldiers would not tolerate him for much longer and some grievous harm would come to him. I agreed to admit him but insisted that he should be locked in one of our cellars as he was continuing to direct the most awful oaths towards the soldiers. The cellars had been prepared for the most difficult and violent lunaticks, and those who needed to be restrained, though they were as yet unused. The soldiers escorted Bob to the west cellar, and he seemed quite pleased to see such a simple cell, with its dry, soft straw. His demeanour quietened as soon as the soldiers left, and he immediately turned his back on us, lay down and went to sleep.

I sent a message to my friend John Lougher, who arranged for a physician of his acquaintance, Benjamin Wrench, to attend the next morning, which he duly did. He took considerable time to assess our unusual visitor, and then reported that, though the man would only give his name as Bob and would give no account of his settlement, he was in good physical health, though quite out of his wits. Doctor Wrench not only refused any offer of payment for his services; he also provided one of his men to stay with us in case Bob turned violent again. In fact, Bob was quite peaceable for as long as he was left alone; he would pace about muttering to himself, or in his quieter moments he would sit in one corner of the cellar, reading from his book. He became agitated again when we had to move him to freshen his cell, and then I was pleased for the presence of Doctor Wrench's man.

Bob stayed with us for several weeks whilst we argued with the courts as to who should take responsibility for him, as he was not a resident of our city. Disputes between parishes about these wandering lunaticks were common, and, over the years, I took in many of these unfortunates, men and women, with no real abode, or family, but who, for the most part, seemed content to walk between our towns and villages. I made room for the ones who were deprived of their senses if I could; most recovered after a period of rest and care and some good food, and then they were always keen to resume their wanderings. I never let it be known that I let them stay, for we would have been quite overwhelmed. My official position was that we would only take those lunaticks who were proven to be residents of Norwich. But on occasion, if space allowed, I let Christian charity guide me, for, if treated with kindness, they were usually very little trouble.

As the weeks passed, Bob appeared to be sometimes in his wits, sometimes out, and we kept him confined. He slept a lot, but always awoke when his meals arrived. Finally, the court established that Bob was a resident of Diss, a town some distance away, and that he should be taken back there. We had warned Bob that he needed to leave, but when the authorities came to collect him he pointedly refused to go with them, stating firmly, 'Those plague-sores will have to carry me out,' then he promptly sat down on the floor. He refused to move and Doctor Wrench's man and two other attendants from the authorities had to carry him through the house to a waiting carriage. They had some difficulty, though Bob stayed calm enough as he reclined between them and gave us a cheery wave as he passed through the door. When the orderlies cleaned his cell they found a book, a kind of diary, and among the extracts written therein was the following:

EPITAPH

Here lies the body of a young man of Diss,
Who vowed he would never accept marital bliss.
He would neither work, nor take, nor give,
And died because he was too lazy to live.

I read no more of his personal thoughts and, after giving it a quick wipe-over, I put Bob's book safely on my shelf, ready to return to him. Sadly, it is there still for I have heard no more of Bob and it appears that his familiar figure has been lost from the streets of Norwich.

RUTH

Another poor soul in need of sanctuary was Ruth (as I shall call her) – a well-to-do woman of about my age. Faith was still our only resident, and I was reluctant to accept another patient, but I felt a connection with this woman – perhaps acknowledging that, without the love of my beloved, my Samuel, I might have been in need of such care myself. With my constant faith in God, I chose to believe that I, too, would have met with similar kindness. I hope so; in any case, I saw a chance to do good. Ruth was from a very prominent family in the county, and they could certainly afford to place her in a private hospital, but she had travelled with her husband from a town near the coast in North Norfolk, hearing that we offered hope of a cure. Ruth was aware of the start of her own descent into the worst type of madness, the sort that often resulted in a person being shackled for their own safety, and where they usually remained for the rest of their tragic lives. She was aware that this was her likely fate and came to us, hoping we could offer her an alternative. She had arrived during one of her more lucid times and was able to explain that she had seen a similar pattern of behaviour in her own mother and other of her kin and feared she would suffer the eventual decline into 'a raving lunatick', as she herself described it. Not wishing for her family to observe her in that state, she requested that we admit her. I agreed that she could stay with us for a period of three months while we assessed her to see if there was any likelihood of a cure, but that we would have to insist that she leave if her condition proved untreatable. Ruth reassured her husband that she was joining us of her own free will and that she would be well treated, but that she did not wish him to visit her again until she was fully recovered. He agreed, looking quite upset, and paid a substantial amount of money towards her keep and left her with us, there and then.

As she had feared, Ruth descended into a darkness where she was deeply suspicious of all people, even though she had come to know us well. She saw 'signs from the Devil' in all sorts of ordinary things, once even screaming that the flame of her candle had burnt blue and caused her to fear that the Devil was standing over her. Though we patiently explained that this was simply an old superstition, she refused to re-enter her sleeping room, and for the sake of our peace and her relief we moved her into another room. We found that as long as someone was with her, to reassure her during her wildest times, we never had cause to restrain her. I asked Mistress Blackthorn, the soldier boy's mother, whom I saw from time to time, if she would help me and take it in turns to sit with Ruth, and she was pleased to oblige, for some welcome payment and time away from her gloomy lodgings. After many weeks we could see that Ruth was slowly returning to her senses, and eventually we were able to call for her family to collect her. While waiting for the carriage to take her home and as we said goodbye, Ruth made me promise that we would accept her back if she ever had need. I readily agreed, wishing, of course, to offer her some solace, and to continue to do good.

The Bethel was quieter after Ruth had returned home. She had been quite demented at her worst, but as she improved it was possible to converse for a while with her, and I missed our chats; Faith occupied herself, and Ellen was going through one of her quieter periods, wanting her own company and staying in her room most of the time. So I was feeling a little lonely, but one day, as I sat with my window open, I closed my eyes and I could hear the most harmonious sound of bells coming from the church of St Peter Mancroft. I was told that it was the first time a full peal of 5,040 changes had been rung in England. I must have entered a kind of trance for it was over three hours later that I opened my eyes as the final chimes rang out. I'm sure I was not asleep, though the time had passed not altogether slowly, and I had not thought of my worries at all. I felt quite refreshed and also found I had developed an appetite. I got up and hurried downstairs in search of Mrs Crick, hoping for one of her little sweet cakes that I had become rather partial to.

Another winter descended, and my friend, John Hall, visited to tell me of the sad death of his beloved son, Thomas, whom I had known since a boy. Only a few short months earlier, John Hall had been so excited to tell me that his son had become a captain in the Artillery Company, which had been raised in consequence of the rebellion in the North. We had both been proud that Thomas, and others in Norwich, had quickly formed a force for the protection of our great country. We had been reassured that some patriotic spirit still existed, despite everyone being quite worn out by endless war, but, of course, with this tragic news, I wished that Thomas had not been so quick to volunteer to fight.

I paid my respects at Thomas's funeral at the church of St George's of Colegate, on a dark December day. It was a very grand affair, a little too showy in my opinion, but fitting his father's status, as former mayor and lieutenant colonel of the Militia Regiment (where my late father was a captain, many years ago). Various people attended, many out of genuine respect for the poor boy's father, but also some who were there just to see the spectacle. It was quite a sight to witness – before the corpse went thirty-four boys, being the number of the years of his age; they were followed by the city clergy, then six bachelors who supported the pall. The procession was closed by the Artillery Company, near 100 in number, I heard, who were all in black cloaks, with laced hats, swords, white gloves and silk knots.

I certainly do not wish for such a funeral when my time comes – I have plans for the minimum of fuss – but I hope it gave his father a little solace. I did approve of the funeral sermon, though, from Revelation xiv. v.13, and preached by the Reverend Mr John Clark:

> *And I heard a voice from heaven saying unto me… Blessed are the dead which die in the Lord from henceforth: Yea, saith the Spirit, that they may rest from their labours; and their works do follow them…*

I was informed that Thomas had left several legacies, including £200 to the Bethel Hospital, and I was honoured that he saw fit to remember my House, perhaps after seeing his father's involvement in my endeavours. When John Hall next visited he was quieter and had lost some of his vitality, and we just talked and then simply sat in silence, looking out over the gardens towards the city walls as the sky darkened. And, though I could not truly understand his suffering, of a parent having lost a child, I could at least be with him in his time of need – my worthy and most faithful friend.

Ten

'WITH DUE REGARD AS WELL TO SOULS AS BODIES'

'Tis also requir'd that the Master... be a Man that lives in the Fear of God and sets up true Protestant Religion in his Family and will have a due Regard as well to souls as bodies of those that are under his care

The harsh winter chill had finally released its icy grip on our city and there was peace in our little sanctuary, our Bethel. Ellen was calm, and Faith had settled in well, though our rooms were still empty. We had our routines, our quiet days and settled nights. I was sleeping well, and my cough had improved, and though I saw no return of my previous vigour, I was getting by.

We all felt a little of the hope and promise that comes with the longer days of spring, and on the sixth day of March, at about seven o'clock in the evening, a quite glorious event occurred. I was about to retire to my room, and, as I slowly climbed the staircase, I looked out to the north of the city and there appeared a very strange and unusual sight, a little above the horizon. I called to Mrs Crick and the maids, and for a time we watched as the wondrous fierce and fiery lights shimmered and swirled across the night sky. I had to calm the impending hysteria of the younger of the maids who was exhibiting an annoying weakness of spirit, quite overwhelmed by the sight that filled her eyes. I patiently reassured her that the great display was a force of nature, not a sign of doom emanating from God. A dear friend, who had an interest in scientific matters, had earlier told me the nature of this phenomenon – an aurora borealis – what beautiful words. But even my detailed explanation did not calm the silly girl and I asked Mrs Crick, who was looking a little uncertain herself, to take her to the kitchen, away from the windows and, I thought to myself, well away from me.

I stood there, then, quite alone, for a very long time while the ever-changing colours covered the sky and gladdened my very heart and soul, and I felt a deep sense of peace for the first time in months. I stood at the window for a few more nights to observe more of the same nature (though none had the same fierceness as that first night), and I felt a calm strength slowly descend upon me. The dreadful lethargy that had weighed upon me since I had moved into the Bethel started to lift. As the fiery sky began to fade on the last night, and with resurfaced memories of my dear Sam, I hurried to my room as fast as my bony little legs could carry me, full of a rediscovered feeling of joy and possibility. I searched through Samuel's chest for the instructions I had produced many years before; my plans of how I had intended to run the Bethel and to care for the lunaticks. Then I spent many nights sat at my table reconsidering and rewriting them, able to plan in more detail now that the Bethel and its rooms were real and waiting to be filled.

And so, with my energy restored, I knew I was finally ready. I decided to welcome the disturbed souls of Norwich into my House, well, some of them at least. I appointed three trustworthy men, recommended by my friend, John Lougher, as attendants for the male lunaticks, for I had learnt from my experience with Bob that an appearance of strength was sometimes useful. I also took on two stout, older women, who had a calm and capable manner, for the female lunaticks. At first, we only admitted those suffering from melancholy, or requiring simple care, but my House soon became a busy place, as we all got used to our new residents and they to us. I was encouraged that the attendants, our maids and Mrs Crick showed them a great deal of kindness and patient understanding. It was a gentle introduction to the world of the mad for many of the people I had employed, and I knew it would prove useful when we took on the more disturbed and violent lunaticks. I hope I set a good example in my dealings with those first residents, though I have to say they were not at all demanding – most were quite tragic souls, simply wanting a little peace and escape from their weary lives. I was able to manage by supervising the attendants myself, but I found it tiring, and I knew that, in due course, I would need to appoint a master of the House for the day-to-day running of the Bethel.

My joy at seeing the Bethel finally being used for its true purpose was short-lived, for, as we moved through another bleak and tiresome winter, I was again afflicted by an illness that would affect me for the rest of my days. The ache in my bones would not abate, and for a while I felt I was reaching the end of my time on earth. I was fairly content for I had succeeded in building the Bethel, and we had accepted our first lunaticks, though I was saddened that I would probably not live to see it being used more fully as a sanctuary for those truly disturbed of mind.

I struggled on for a while but eventually, over a year after we had first opened our doors, I was forced to make it known about the city that, due to my recurring ill health, we were not accepting new residents. Some of our first lunaticks had become well enough to return home, but a few were not fit to be discharged and so they stayed with us. I had to allow some of our attendants to find other positions as there was not enough work to fully employ them. The soldier boy's mother also left, for, though I had offered her a permanent room with us, she reluctantly declined, unable to live so close to the site of her son's execution. Thankfully, Mrs Crick had overcome most of her earlier fears of the mad and announced that she would be remaining at the Bethel, adding that she was concerned about who would look after us if she left. I am grateful to her for caring, and for the wholesome meals she prepared. Edward Brightwell stayed, too, most appreciative of the hot supper he shared each evening with Mrs Crick.

Sadly, half of the rooms were locked up once again, and it was a quiet time. Yet, outside, the rose garden bloomed, the columbine seeded and spread, and the honeysuckle clambered in all directions over the boundary walls. Even the apple tree that we had planted in memory of the young soldier had begun to bear fruit.

Despite seeing this new life all around me, I had to accept that I was getting older; I certainly felt quite ancient. I had a notion that I was holding on to life simply because I could not face the torment that my passing would cause my poor Ellen. Though I tried to hide my ill health from her, for fear of causing her any distress, secretly I was making preparations. I had concluded that I should hand over the running of the Bethel to those more able than I, and hence, as I continued to get weaker, the arrangements for this became a matter of urgency.

CONCERNS ABOUT THE DETAILS OF MY LAST WILL AND TESTAMENT

It was 1717 and I had lived for seventy long years. I had seen much death and despair, and I had been tempted to give in to my grief after the loss of my beloved Samuel, but I had found my strength, I had persevered, and I had built my House. Seeing the good we had started to do had made me adamant that it would continue to provide sanctuary, for ever after. Whilst trying, fruitlessly it seemed, to recover my health, I thought deeply about who should run the Bethel after my death. I had learnt, over the years, whom I could depend upon, and to that end I invited those loyal and trusted men to call on me. I proposed to explain my desire for the creation of a charitable trust or foundation, to ensure that the Bethel would continue after I was gone, and to ask my dear friends if I could name them as future trustees, under the terms of my will.

I discussed my plans first with my great friend John Hall, who appeared pleased to be asked, then I requested of Mr William

Cockman that he be the sole executor of my will, and also a trustee, and he, too, agreed. Next, I talked to Timothy Ganning, a freeman and upholsterer by trade, whom I had known for many years as the second son of the rector of Barnham Broom, an acquaintance of Samuel's. When Mr Ganning visited I was rather moved to spend a little time talking of his father, and of Samuel, before explaining my proposal. I had high regard for Mr Ganning for he was a little less concerned with the trappings of high office than many of his contemporaries. Indeed, a few years earlier he had been discharged from his position as sheriff, upon payment of the usual fine of eighty pounds, which I heard he was happy to pay, in order that he could return to his former life and live more quietly, which he preferred. I watched out of the window as Mr Ganning walked away from the Bethel and noticed that he stopped to talk to Mr John Lombe and his brother William, whom I had also asked to call upon me. They were both persons of position and influence, as merchants and members of the Worsted Weavers Company, my father's own guild. Unsurprisingly, when they arrived they were expecting my request and readily agreed. The following day, John Thompson and Richard Cooke, who had been recommended by my friend John Hall, duly accepted and so my list of trustees was complete.

Many of the men I had named in my will, who I prayed would see fit to run the Bethel according to my instructions, after my death, were men who had been conspicuous in serving this city by undertaking its onerous offices – aldermen, sheriff, mayor. Some had been quite vocal about the support they had given me, and the benevolence they had shown my House and its occupants; maybe, to my mind, a little lacking in humility at times, but nevertheless, if they benefited from their shared duty to me, then so be it. I, too, had benefited, not only from my friendships with these powerful and influential men but also from my father's name and reputation.

I have been told I am a strong woman; I have certainly always had a determined mind, but I know I would not have been able to build my House without the support of those men, not in our times. Such is the way of things, though I still hope that the world, and the people in it, will continue to develop, and that women will one day be considered genuine equals of men. For now, perhaps we should be proud that the Bethel stands, because we have worked together, women and men, to create this place.

With all this in mind, and with the agreement of my trusted and faithful friends, I finalised my will, seven pages long, signed and witnessed. I had written out several drafts for I did not want to miss a single detail, until, finally, I was satisfied. My will made clear my intention that the Bethel would endure after my death so that the poor lunaticks in Norwich would continue to receive kindness and understanding, for ever after. To that end, aside from a few personal bequests, I had left my entire fortune to my trustees, and I had faith that they would use it well.

EXCERPT FROM THE WILL OF MARY CHAPMAN, FOURTH DAY OF DECEMBER 1717

And whereas it hath pleased Almighty God to visit and afflict some of my nearest relations and kindred with lunacy, but has hitherto blessed me with the use of my reason and understanding, as a monument of my thankfulness unto God for this invaluable mercy and out of a deep sense of His divine goodness and undeserved love to me vouchsafed and in compassion to the deplorable state of such persons as are deprived of the exercise of their reason and understanding and are destitute of relations or friends to take care of them and also because it was much upon my good husband's thoughts to contribute something towards perpetual maintenance of this particular act of Charity, for all and every of these reasons my Will is that the House I have lately built in the Parish of St Peter Mancroft... shall by my said trustees... from time to time for ever after be used and employed for the convenient reception and habitation of poor lunaticks which it shall be called according to the desire of my well beloved husband by the name of Bethel...

... And that such person or persons as are afflicted with lunacy or madness (not such as are fools or idiots from their birth) and are poor inhabitants in the said City of Norwich or elsewhere shall be from time to time put into the said House by appointment under writing of my Trustees...

... And the care, maintenance, and relief of them for clothes, food and physick, and all other necessaries shall be under the direction, order and management of my said Trustees and their successors for ever... further, is that such lunatick persons... in the said House shall be kept close and not suffered to wander abroad during their disorder, nor shall they continue in the said House any longer than their lunacy or madness is upon them and they be restored to possession of themselves, but after that shall be removed...

Once the matter of my will was settled, I felt as though a great weight had been lifted from me – my health finally improved despite the cold winter nights and I was steadier on my feet and looking forward to the spring once more. Feeling quite sprightly, I decided to open the doors of the Bethel once again. We immediately had requests for help from many families of the disturbed, who told me they had been dismayed when we had stopped accepting new residents. As word spread, we even woke one morning to find a small group of lunaticks, accompanied by their kin, on our doorstep, waiting patiently, hopeful of a room in my House.

At once, I started to organise. I arranged deliveries of fire wood and fresh straw, I made enquiries and, thankfully, we were able to take back most of our former attendants, who quickly settled into their old routines and duties. Mrs Crick took on some new kitchen maids and got them to work; they visited the market to increase their regular orders and came back laden with the makings of her pottages and pies. Throughout our quiet time, Mr Brightwell had kept the garden immaculate and there was little extra for him to do as the House came back to life. Yet he was pleased that there would be more of a use for the vegetables and fruit and herbs that he had been cultivating, and he arrived regularly at the door of Mrs Crick's kitchen holding his freshly harvested bounty. Everything else was already prepared and waiting. All that was needed was for the windows to be opened and the rooms to be freshened. In a few short days, having first admitted our doorstep lunaticks, I was able to walk around and feel again the joy of seeing our rooms and corridors and garden filling up once more.

AN UNLIKELY FRIENDSHIP WITH BENJAMIN WRENCH

Quite unexpectedly, I made a rather unusual friend, the great and wealthy, and quite hefty, though rather pleasing to the eye, Benjamin Wrench. His father, John Wrench, was well known in this city, and a contemporary of my own father, though I could not claim they were friends. John Wrench was one of the leading citizens of Norwich, as sheriff in 1669 and mayor in 1683. He had attended my father's funeral and, as a mark of respect, I attended his when he passed this life just two years later. Maybe that is why his son, Benjamin, seemed to have time for me. We met after a church service when I overheard heard him talking about the Bethel. I paused, ducking behind a pillar, curious to hear what he was saying, but he spotted me and enthusiastically introduced me to his companions, a Lord and Lady Something. We chatted for a while about my endeavours and I recalled that he had, of course, kindly attended one of my first residents, Bob, the vagrant from Diss. Then, feeling a little out of my depth amongst such people of title, I politely took my leave. However, he bounded up to me as I passed under the tower of St Peter Mancroft, keen to tell me that he was pleased I had recovered my health and that the Bethel was once again serving its true purpose. I was a little flustered by his attentions, but then, to my delight, the great Benjamin Wrench offered me his services as visiting physician, at least until I could find a permanent replacement. No longer flustered, I accepted immediately, and so began our rather unlikely friendship.

The Wrenches are an immensely influential family, and I had always considered them given too much to ostentatious displays of their wealth and not enough to God for my liking – but I quickly revised my opinion, of Benjamin Wrench at least, for I have come to know him well. It is certainly true that he likes to be married – three times at last count – and he has succeeded in getting all his children married into other titled families. He is lord of the manor of Little Melton and still drives in his four-in-hand from his country residence, Mangreen Hall, to his house in Norwich. He is renowned for dressing well, and can be recognised at a distance, his red silk stockings showing brightly beneath his knee breeches. He is loud and sure of himself, with that sense of entitlement of the upper classes that stifles comment or criticism. As an elderly widow, though, I have my own sense of entitlement, and I make sure that at times he is quiet so that I, too, can have my say. Somehow, against all perceived wisdom, we seem to have built up a mutual respect. In private he is more thoughtful than you would guess from his rather exuberant person, and he has always been very generous of his time, advising me about the medical care of our residents. Even the apothecaries, who usually move in their own time, act fast to provide the physicks he prescribes. Not only has he attended our patients without asking for payment; he has also shown much kindness to them, and I am grateful for his dedication. He has a way with words, too, and charms the usually quite unflappable Mrs Crick, who presents herself without fail in a fresh apron, holding a plate of his favourite fancies, whenever he visits.

Despite having seen for myself his true goodness of spirit and knowing how busy he was with all his other commitments, to say nothing of his social engagements, I hesitated to ask him to become one of the trustees of the Bethel. However, one afternoon, after spending some time with our most demanding lunaticks, he came and threw himself down in one of my quite delicate chairs (which, thankfully, stood up to the onslaught rather well), then, barely suppressing a belch, he proceeding to talk at me. I do so love his enthusiasm, but, for a gentleman, he is not as careful with his manners as he could be. When he first visited I had to remind him that I was not partial to the odours of his previous meal, and, thenceforth, he made sure to unburden himself in the hallway. I always forgive him these lapses, though, he has many female admirers, and even I am not immune. I observed, too, with a small smile, as he repositioned his long limbs, without the least display of grace, and quite obscuring the cushion, that, for a fine-looking man, he is rather ungainly.

As to the matter of being a trustee, he gently declined. However, he promised, most sincerely, that, if called upon by the future trustees, he would act as physician to the Bethel for as long as he was able, and I believe that he will remain true to his word.

As it happened, I had reason to call the great Benjamin Wrench sooner than I had expected, for again, without warning, another lunatick arrived on our doorstep…

'MAD-RAGS'

One of my most memorable lunatics was an aged woman who was well known to all who lived or worked in and around the Bethel. We heard a tale that she had been born into a wealthy family from Cambridge and had married well, but that, following the death of her husband, her mental state had quickly deteriorated. Her children promptly had her certified as insane, drove her to Norwich, deposited her, without means, on the street, as night fell, and then hurried away to claim their inheritance and start new lives. I do not know if the story was true, and she had been around for so long I doubt if anyone could remember when she first arrived. She lived in a run-down out-house in the grounds of St Peter Mancroft, between the church and the market. She wandered the streets of Norwich from dawn to dusk, in all weathers. She could be heard muttering to an imaginary companion and having conversations that sometimes seemed to be quite reasonable, possibly giving orders to a servant, but which became nonsense when heard close up. If left alone she was not particularly troublesome, and we had all got used to her presence in Norwich. She had developed a begging round and knew where she best stood a chance of a meal for each day of the week, though she was careful not to pester people too often and so fared better than the more belligerent beggars. She was wrapped in layers of a jumble of garments, a mixture of cast-offs and donations by kind parishioners from the church, but always topped by a grubby shawl, its tassels trailing in the mud. I cannot imagine how she managed to endure such a grim life, but evidently she got by.

Children often cruelly taunted her, calling her Mad-Rags in view of her muttering and her hodgepodge of garments. Local people mostly tolerated her, though she was regularly sworn at by visitors to the city. The stagecoach drivers, in particular, disliked her, as she would frequently stand in front of them, delaying their departure, and demand that they put her on the next coach to Cambridge. They claimed she was off-putting to their fares and though she often received a curse and a shove for her troubles she would simply move down the line of drivers hoping for better luck. One dank evening, the London coach came along St Stephen's Street too fast and too close, and she was too slow to move out of the way. She stumbled and slipped in the mud and, unable to get up or put weight onto her leg, she crawled to the side of the street, just out of harm's way. She was found, sometime later by the rector, a friend of mine and, knowing that this poor unfortunate woman would not survive without some sort of medical attention, he supported her sodden, muddied frame as she limped slowly up the hill to our hospital. He asked if she could stay for the night, and of course, with Christian charity, I agreed, and this fragile bundle of a woman, silently accepting the reassurance of the rector, followed him closely through our door. She stood for a while, shocked and unsure of what to do, but seemingly determined to block the poor rector's attempts to leave. We reached a kind of stand-off – this person eyeing us with suspicion and us unable to persuade her to move out of the doorway, so we could at least close the door and prevent curious passers-by from observing this entertainment – 'the mad in the madhouse'. Thankfully, Faith appeared, and with her sweet face and kind voice she was able to gently lead the poor woman a little further into the hallway, allowing the rector to slip past with a relieved wave of the hand, his duty done. We were unable to persuade her to remove her muddy rags and she would not move into one of our sleeping rooms, though she did eat some bread, greedily washed down with a mug of ale, which she then waved at us, demanding a refill. She settled down to sleep on the tiled floor of the entrance hall, her muddy rags wrapped in the fresh, clean, blankets that Faith had set beside her.

My dear Doctor Wrench, who was fortunately in the city, visited the next day and diagnosed a sprain in her ankle, all the while managing to ignore the loathsome condition she was in. While waiting for her ankle to mend, she remained in our entrance hall, sitting near to the door, looking out onto the street. As soon as she was able, she would leave our House in the morning to go on her usual rounds, always returning at night to sleep, making sure that Faith was inside before she would settle. Faith eventually wore her down with kindness and persuaded her to remove her layers of rotting, stinking garments, and we saw that underneath she was no more than a tiny stick of a woman, though not badly nourished – no doubt as a result of her begging round and her new-found fondness for our ale. Pushing aside our offer of a bowl of warm water and soap, she took her time to pick over some clothes from a pile we had left in the hall to tempt her, discarding many that were not to her satisfaction. Finally, when she was happy with her choice, she donned those carefully chosen garments, rebuilding her layers. She topped them with her dirty old shawl, which she had torn out of the hands of our attendant who had tried to remove it, at arm's length, along with her other rank rags. On closer examination the shawl was made of the finest cloth, richly coloured, though dimmed with dirt, and with an exquisite butterfly pattern. We saw that it had the letter 'S' embroidered in one corner, and so decided to call her Sarah, for I would not allow her to be called by the insulting nickname she was known by on the street. Maybe we guessed her name correctly, for sometimes she even responded to our greetings. I presumed her shawl had once belonged to one of the rich ladies who loiter uselessly about our city, and was acquired by Sarah, who, on occasion, was no more honest than she needed to be. Happy with her new attire, Sarah graciously bowed her head to us, by way of thanks, and then set off on her daily travels once more.

Sarah always refused to venture much further into the House, preferring to stay close to the front door. Faith had the idea of clearing a small store room just off the entrance hall, and Sarah deigned to move in, much to our relief, for she was a little off-putting to those visitors who met with her presence soon after their arrival. We also finally persuaded her to have a wash – more of a wipe-over, if truth be told, but it served to freshen the air at least. Sarah's demeanour did improve with our constant kind words, gently spoken as we passed by, going about our daily business. Whilst she would always look for Faith, she became most attached to Mrs Crick, our cook, who took to calling her Lady Sarah. This seemed to please her, and now and then she would start to respond in a very polite manner before losing her way and lapsing into her muttering once again.

Sarah stayed with us for some years until early one morning she was found next to her favourite herring pie stall in the market, quite dead. I cannot truly say that we cured her in any way, but it just seemed right that she became one of our residents. After all, Samuel had strongly believed we should open our doors to the poorest of lunaticks, those who had nowhere else to turn, and I am certain he would have approved. I can also picture him, perhaps after a day spent at the library, strolling through the market and stopping at the pie stall, then returning here, with a pie in each pocket, passing one to Sarah as he walked through the hallway. But… forgive me, I am dreaming of Samuel again, and the life we might have had, and that will never do. In any case, we never did find out the reason for the torment underneath that poor woman's ragged exterior, though I have come to believe that the sad distraction of her mind was precipitated in some way by tragic circumstances. Looking back, perhaps the butterfly shawl was indeed a treasured possession, for she was clearly so attached to it. I wondered sometimes if the stories about her were true – was that scrap of material a sad reminder of her previous life?

1719, A YEAR OF LOSS

With my vigour wholly restored, we continued to accept more people into our care and there was not an empty room to be found in the Bethel, for, as one lunatic was discharged, another took their place. Ruth had returned to us each time her madness descended, but sadly her periods of clarity were becoming shorter and we were learning that after each episode her recovery took increasingly longer to achieve. Despite our best efforts, I could see that she often struggled to recognise us, and it was becoming more difficult to converse sensibly with her. Though I had proposed that this hospital would only accept those for whom there was the expectation of a cure, I had little hope that she would ever fully regain her senses, but I could not turn Ruth away – she had become a part of our lives and this place.

We said a sad goodbye to Faith. I thought she would be with us always, but then, one day, she entered my room, sat down beside me and took my hand. Looking into my eyes, she declared herself 'cured' and announced that she was ready to move on. It was not long after her parents had died, in quick succession, events that I had feared would precipitate a decline in Faith but which had, in fact, released her from the prospect of an unwanted marriage, and so eased her troubled mind. She was quite capable of caring for herself, and of making her own decisions, so there was no reason for her to stay with us, if she chose to leave. At Faith's insistence, Doctor Wrench certified her as no longer deprived of her senses. On receipt of this declaration, the court had to accept that Faith was of sound mind, and hence she was able to inherit her parents' fortune. Though I was too old and had seen too much suffering to usually waste my energy on tears, I surprised myself, and, indeed, we both cried when she left.

I do not know what happened to Faith. I do know that she left the city. I have not heard of any reports of her death, and I pray for her and hope she is able to live a long and happy life. Some months after she left, I opened a letter containing a short note, stating simply 'Thank you', which caused me to reach for my handkerchief. There was also a large donation, which I used to create two additional rooms in the Bethel, thereby helping a few more 'Faiths'. Perhaps I could consider her one of our successes after all.

Not long after Faith left us, I was faced with the unexpected death of my beloved sister. It took me some time to recover from the loss of two of my dearest companions, though I tried to carry on as usual. I was heartened that Faith was well enough to leave and start a new life, and I was gladdened, too, that Ellen was finally at rest, though she had been constantly by my side for most of my life, and I felt the loss of her for the rest of my days.

Her death took me by surprise as I tended to forget that, as I had aged, so had Ellen, for she continued to be quite innocent and childlike in her ways, even up to her death. I was consoled that she did not outlive me, and that I was with her at the end. She quietly took to her bed one day, complaining, unusually for her, of feeling unwell, never to rise again. In her final days she seemed unaware that she was dying – in fact, she was the most serene I had ever known her to be, perhaps because, finally, she was able to give up the fight. On that last evening, she asked me to lie on the bed beside her and to tell her the stories of my day, as we had done so many years before as young girls, and I had talked and talked, gently and slowly. I told her about the comings and goings of our friends here at the Bethel, and then repeated my father's stories, as best as I could remember. I talked of our mother and her love for us, of our trips to the market, of my life with Samuel, and, of course, of her raid on the rectory garden, and we giggled again. As I started to repeat her favourite stories once more, I heard her breathing deepen, though as I turned to her I could see that her eyes were still bright, still looking at me, urging me to continue. I think that, as her time on this earth drew to a close, she could not hear my words, but I do believe she could somehow feel me talking and so I carried on, even after her eyes had closed for the final time. Ellen's passing was one of the gentlest deaths I have ever witnessed, and I am grateful, as most of her life had been a trial to her, and I praise God that he granted her that peace, at her end.

I had not expected at all that Ellen's passing would make me mourn once again my other losses – my darling mother, the immense presence that was my father, and my beloved Samuel. Even so, with all that I had seen, I accepted that death was a natural part of life, and as I awaited the end of my own path through this world I gave thanks to God for making my much-loved family the centre of that life – though, I confess, I was lonely, more than ever.

My dear friend Benjamin Wrench called on me soon after Ellen's death to pay his respects, for he was not able to attend her funeral. He brought a gift, a copy of Sir Thomas Browne's

Christian Morals, which he thought might provide some solace, and, if I had had the strength to read it all, it should certainly have distracted me for some time, for it was a demanding text. I still pick it up, now and again, and read a little; more comforted by Benjamin's kind thought than the words on the page.

I was still visited by Hannah, who was as calm and reassuring as ever, and she recommended a friend of hers, the Widow Taylor, who was in need of a place to stay, and could act as my companion until I regained my strength. It seemed a reasonable proposition and I was willing to try and tolerate this person. We agreed for her to visit to see if we would be compatible, though I feared a new person might not be able to bear my little routines, and I was becoming irritated before she even arrived. I admit, though, that I was somewhat intrigued by the feisty little person who turned up. So intrigued, in fact, that she is here still.

The Widow Taylor has seemingly had quite a sad life, though I do not press her for details as she says she prefers not to look to the past, and I can feel that, like me, she is a survivor. Outwardly rather dour, she has a cutting sense of humour that still takes me by surprise and makes me laugh out loud. Her no-nonsense approach soon had me up and about, as I obediently followed her instructions to eat regularly and to put my books aside and retire to bed early each night. I had always thought that I was a forthright person, but I had met my match. I expected to have to explain so much to her, not least my vision for the Bethel, but I think she could already see it. I know she loves this House, not only as a sanctuary for her but, somehow, she fits here too.

I was keen that we should open our doors to some of the more deranged of our city's troubled souls. To that end, and on the recommendation of my friend John Hall, I appointed Henry Harston to manage the day-to-day organisation of the Bethel. He had no medical expertise or particular knowledge of caring for lunaticks – instead, he was responsible for the attendants and orderlies, and employed reliable and capable men to do repairs and general maintenance, thus ensuring our residents were comfortable and kept away from harm.

On his very first day, I informed Mr Harston that I had drawn up some general rules and principles for the care of our residents. Many of the attendants had worked here for long enough to know the standards of care that I expected; even so, I felt it would be useful for Mr Harston to know that I insisted that everyone should treat our lunaticks well. Standing directly in front of him, to make sure he was giving me his full attention, I read out my list:

> Above all, the lunatics will be treated with kindness and understanding. Any odd behaviours that they may display will be treated with tolerance, and they will not be ridiculed. They will not be subjected to any form of violent correction, and only the most gentle means may be used to control any disorderly lunaticks. Restraint may only be used for the most violent and uncontrollable lunaticks, and I must be informed immediately if a lunatick needs to be conveyed to the cellars. The attendants will be kept in absolute ignorance as to who are and who are not paying for their treatment, so that all our residents are treated equally. All residents will have their hands and faces washed each day, and they will have clean clothing when needed. Those who require it will have assistance in getting up and going to bed. Their bedding and rooms will be kept clean and fresh, as will the communal rooms. The master is responsible for ensuring the lunaticks are safely in their sleeping rooms at night, and that the doors and gates of the Bethel are secured. You will also ensure that our residents are protected against fire, self-injury, assault and escape. Meals will be served at regular times, and these will be plain but full of goodness. Residents who cannot manage to feed themselves will be assisted. Mrs Crick should be informed if any of our residents have any

particular needs, for example she will prepare softer foods for our older, toothless residents if they struggle to chew. All lunaticks will be encouraged to spend some time in the day room, and to take a turn around the garden if the weather permits. They will join our daily service to give thanks to God, accompanied by their attendants. Any illness or injury will be reported to myself or the Widow Taylor, so that the physician can be called. Physick will be obtained from the apothecary, under the guidance of the physician. Relatives of our residents are encouraged to visit, as long as their presence does not cause any distress. On no account will people be allowed into the Bethel to 'view' our lunaticks, for whilst they are under our care they must not be subjected to any cruel exploitation. I do not tolerate such behaviour and I charge the master of this House to ensure that any such lapses in care are dealt with immediately and severely.

As I paused, Mr Harston looked rather overwhelmed and seemed to be struck dumb, so I started to read my list again, whereupon he quickly regained his voice and assured me that he did understand my requirements and their importance. I held up my hand to stop him moving away, and, to make it perfectly clear, I repeated, 'The lunaticks in my House will be treated with compassion and understanding. At all times.' He nodded and reassured me again of his kind intentions. As I watched him saunter away, I felt that perhaps I would keep a close eye on Mr Harston. I was old and did not appear particularly terrifying, perhaps, but I could still make sure that everyone carried out their duty in all aspects of the care they provided, and that included Mr Harston.

After that first day, I had several conversations with Mr Harston about my requirements for the master of this House. I was unsure at first if he truly shared my vision for the Bethel, but he appeared to be an efficient type, and was a follower, he assured me, of the true Protestant religion. I planned to remind Mr Harston from time to time that John Hall was one of our benefactors and that he called upon me regularly, when, of course, he would be able to check that Mr Harston was performing his duties to my satisfaction.

Once I was free of many of my former responsibilities, I found I had more time to consider how we could improve the lives of our residents whilst they were under our roof. From the start, I had been determined to provide our lunaticks with wholesome fare, for I was convinced that good food could, in some way, assist in the healing of their minds. Mrs Crick had proven herself to be a trustworthy and competent cook, and I decided to allow her to run her own kitchen. She would delegate the meal preparation and cooking to her kitchen maids, though under her strict supervision, of course. She would be responsible for planning meals and ordering the necessary ingredients, and keep all receipts and bills and give them to the Widow Taylor, who was helping me with the accounts. Mrs Crick was an exceptional cook, but we often had the same food two or three days in a row, and, therefore, I advised her that we needed more variety, to prevent boredom and to encourage the lunaticks to eat – she was to use any leftovers for suppers, of course, as I detest waste.

I met with her weekly at first to discuss her proposals, and I provided her with the instructions for my own dishes. I thought the ones I used when Samuel's parishioners were in poor health would be particularly useful, including, of course, the possets that I made each day during Samuel's sudden and dreadful decline. I could see that they eased his throat and provided him with a little sustenance, but sadly, even though they had been made with love, they couldn't save him… but… Oh, Lord, I am getting distracted again, as I tend to do now. It is really quite simple, God had called him – I must remember that, and concentrate, for now, on all the good I can still do – and on getting my story told …

Though I retained overall control, I was relieved to hand over some of the more onerous tasks to Mr Harston, and to the

Widow Taylor, who organised the maids and kept her beady eyes on the female lunaticks and their attendants. I continued to make my regular rounds to check that everything was in place, and ensure everyone was working as they should be, as my presence evidently kept people busy. Every day, at a different time, I put on my stern face and walked around, holding my Bible, and a small piece of paper, on which I recorded any failings that needed to be addressed; in truth, I had cause to write very little, but I carried on the pretence for it seemed to get people moving. More often I noticed small acts of kindness towards our residents and always made sure to acknowledge them with the person concerned. I also met with the relatives of the lunaticks to assess their reasons for admittance, then arranged for an examination by our physician, and decided if there was to be a fee and how much was due. In that way, I controlled who was to be admitted, according to our capacity and with consideration to the needs of our existing residents.

'WITH DUE REGARDS AS WELL TO SOULS AS BODIES'

Over the years, I have always insisted that we worship our Lord in a daily service, with the intention of giving the lunaticks hope, through prayer. Sadly, for some, it is about all we can do, despite our constant attempts at cure.

In the early years there were very few of us – often just Faith, my dear Ellen and myself. Mrs Crick and the maids attended their own churches, but sometimes they prayed with us, too. Then Mr Brightwell joined us, for it saved him having to walk to a church outside these walls, and he was also able to pop into the kitchen afterwards for some of Mrs Crick's freshly baked leftovers.

Over the years, as the Bethel has filled with lunaticks, our service has become quite a lively affair. If the weather is fine, we congregate outside, surrounded by God's beauty, or, if wet, we meet in the day room, where, to be honest, it is easier to contain the lunaticks.

Mr Harston is, of course, required to attend for he has always assured me he is a most devout man. However, I had cause to reprimand him at first, for he always had a vitally important reason to be elsewhere. Once, as we were starting to assemble on the lawn, I glanced behind me to see him craftily change direction and move rapidly back towards the House. I tracked him down, and found him sitting behind the straw-house with a pot of ale. I didn't need to say much as he had the grace to look quite shamefaced, but I still reiterated my full list of the requirements for the master of this House – adding that he had a due regard for the souls as well as the bodies of the lunaticks under his care, which meant at the very least that he, and they, must attend our daily service – so then he really understood me and I am pleased to say that he has not missed another service.

I believe it is important that everyone is aware that I am still very much in charge, so I make sure that I lead the service, despite my growing frailty, and it goes like this:

I ask that the attendants assemble the lunaticks under their care; only those who are restrained or unwell are exempt, and I visit them afterwards to read a passage from the Bible – they are not always pleased to see me but I try. I give a reading, taken from Samuel's book of sermons, if I can decipher his scribbles, and we attempt to sing a hymn. If Mr Wood, one of our liveliest lunaticks, is going through one of his excitable phases, he usually joins in with us, singing a hymn of his own choosing, which causes some confusion, though he has a pleasant voice. We struggle through, often all stopping at different times, and ending in a tuneless jumble of hymns, but I do not mind – we are all together, praising God, and that is all that matters. We conclude with prayers, though many of our more distracted lunaticks have often wandered off by that point.

The rector of St Peter Mancroft attends, on occasion, and I respect him for returning, the dear man, for during his first sermon here all the lunaticks found something more entertaining to do, such that by the end there was only him and me, just standing there – he took it well, though he looked rather worn out. I make sure to remind his parishioners, and the great and the good who attend his church, that he is an exceptionally kind man and I appreciate the support he has given the Bethel over the years. I have observed that he is treated with a great deal of respect during the services he leads in his own church – no wandering off allowed there.

1720, A KNIGHT AND A RIOT

My friend Benjamin Wrench was knighted by King George I, in April. There were people in our city who questioned this, given that he held no public office and was not known for his charitable deeds, but I know differently; I know of his kindness and generosity to our residents and of his donations to many of the other worthy causes in Norwich – he just does not talk about his own benevolence, as many of his fellows are inclined to do. I was pleased for him and gave him his due. When we met soon after this great honour was bestowed upon him, he was quite uncharacteristically shy about it, though I noticed he was rather pleased when I congratulated him and addressed him, rather wryly, as Sir Benjamin. For once, despite his quick wit, he had no eloquent response, and was forced to simply accept my compliment, quite graciously, in fact. How I still treasure this most unlikely of friendships – me a feisty, faded, widow, and he a silver-tongued knight.

It was quite an eventful year, first a new knight, and then a riot. On the twentieth day of September, Mr Harston returned from errands in the marketplace and described a disturbance of some sort, which started out of nowhere, caused by a group of men who were intent on destroying all calicoes. An odd reason for a riot, I thought. My friend John Hall, who was with me when

Mr Harston returned, listened with interest, then explained that the cloth manufacturers in Norwich and surrounding areas had become upset by the rich women showing off their gowns, made not of local cloth but from the new printed calicoes, which had been imported from Bengal, no less. The local weavers considered the purchase of these and other East India goods as pernicious to the trade of their own cloths. They had been planning an orderly protest, but a few men, no doubt after spending some hours getting fortified in one of the inns near the market, had suddenly decided to take action, there and then. Mr Harston said he saw some of the rabble entering shops and seizing all the calicoes they found there, much to the consternation of the poor shopkeepers and their customers, and then the parish constables who were called to apprehend the troublemakers were roundly beaten themselves. I should not have laughed, for it was a serious matter, but I had seen how some of those constables treated the lunaticks on our streets, and it was justice of a sort to hear of them getting a taste of their own brutality. With fears that the riot might spread, the Artillery Company was raised, though, of course, once their appearance was threatened, the troublemakers instantly dispersed and were lost amongst the alleyways and backstreets of Norwich.

Mr Harston was quite quivering with indignation (so he said, though he looked suspiciously enlivened), having had to escort two ladies to safety, who, along with many others, had the gowns on their backs cut to pieces. I heard there was much swooning with fright, though no one was actually injured. I suppose it was an entertaining story and I could understand the outrage of our own cloth manufacturers, for they were merely trying to protect their own livelihoods. I'm sure my father would have had something to say about the need for loyalty towards the weavers in our own city, though I'm also sure that he wouldn't have rioted. As to the swooning women, I am pleased to say that I do not acquaint myself with the sort of woman who might be in danger of swooning over anything. Which reminds me – I was rather impressed with Mrs Crick earlier, for I had observed her as she firmly held one of our elderly residents quite still while he had a dislocated shoulder realigned by Sir Benjamin. The glorious Mrs Crick didn't swoon; she just wiped her hands on her apron and marched back to her kitchen. I pray the Lord had mercy on the vegetables she was about to prepare.

BENEFACTIONS

We continued to receive sums of money towards the support of our House. One afternoon, my dear Sir Benjamin paid us a visit and announced his arrival with his usual quiet door banging, before making his way through the lunaticks in the hallway, uttering a reassuring word here and there, to find me, hidden in their midst. He cheerfully pressed twelve pounds and twelve shillings into my rather startled hands. Explaining that he was in a hurry and could not stop, he turned to leave as quietly as he had arrived, then bellowed that he had been given the sum by a person who wished to remain unknown but who very earnestly desired to show his support for my hospital. He turned at the door, and with a smile said, 'Indeed, from a person, Mary, who has not always supported you, or your cause,' then a wink, and he was gone. I was intrigued, thinking perhaps it was the odious suitor I had rejected, but I heard that he still took every opportunity to run me down, so maybe it was from someone who knew one of the poor souls who had benefited from our care, but then, all at once, I was surrounded by lunatics needing my attention and I could not ponder any longer.

Later that month, news reached me of the death of Margaret Hall, wife of my dear friend John Hall, and it saddened me that he had suffered another loss. He visited some days later and informed me that Margaret had bequeathed £100 to the Bethel, in view, he said, of my efforts to understand the mental disorders of women.

I was struck by her generosity. Indeed, I have long questioned the accepted wisdom of the causes of lunacy. I have also thought that perhaps the dreadful feelings of melancholy experienced by some women could, in truth, have a physical basis. Yet mental disorder in women is usually attributed, simply and rather conveniently, to the natural hysteria of females. It is frustrating that the diseases of women are not always taken seriously, but perhaps this is not surprising, for all our physicians are men. Horrifyingly, many of the women who have used their ancient knowledge of herbs and roots to offer treatment and suchlike for the relief of women's ailments have often been cruelly put to death for witchcraft. There is something terribly unfair about the charges brought against these women, who usually have no one to defend them. I am relieved to see that such superstitious nonsense seems to be dying out, at least in the cities, though sadly, even now, we hear of women, often elderly and alone and perhaps with odd ways, still being accused of witchcraft in the villages of Norfolk. I am certain, too, that other women have been put to death for falsified charges, as a means of getting rid of them – I had even considered that it could have been my fate, for there were those who thought I was strange, and disliked the way I defended my lunaticks, but, unlike many of the falsely charged, I have been protected throughout my life, first by my father's good name, and later by my faithful friends, who support me still.

I can think of many women who have stayed with me here, and who, after some time of peace and safety, have recovered and returned to their families – a kinder prospect, I hope, than being locked up, often for all time, in one of the private hospitals. It makes me wonder how many unfortunates have been incarcerated in such places, when perhaps all they needed was some respite from their day-to-day lives and some simple understanding of their unhappiness. That thought renews my strength to carry on, for there are still so many people in need of our kindness, and carry on I must, for as long as God allows.

Most nights now, needing little sleep, I lie awake, fretting about the unfairness of this life, and I pray, fervently, and for longer than ever – for it seems we are in desperate need of more tolerance and understanding in this world.

Eleven

BELOVED LUNATICKS

We are nearly at the end of my story, which is good for I am becoming quite weary.

Today, wrapped up against the cold weather, I walked around the rose garden, noting the tiny buds on the bare stems – a promise of spring to come. I caught sight of my reflection in the window of the day room, and I was shocked at the sight of me, struggling and stooped, for truly I am an old woman now, despite the passions that still burn in my heart. I returned inside and wearily climbed the staircase to my room, then I closed the door firmly behind me, wanting some time alone, to contemplate my life and my endeavours in creating this place…

I know that long years have passed, far too many after Samuel's death, but finally I had fulfilled my promise to him and opened the doors of the Bethel to the lunaticks of Norwich. Of course, I regret that I did not start much sooner, but I know also that I could not have predicted the ferocity of my grief. I remain saddened by all those I could have helped during those lost years. Even now that the Bethel is full of all kinds of lunaticks, it, alone, exists as the one true sanctuary in this city. But clearly my House is not big enough, because I know there are still poor lunaticks who are cruelly confined in the Bridewell or in a workhouse, where there is no understanding, no kindness and certainly no hope of a cure.

I often look back to the early days of the Bethel, and I find solace in the knowledge that some of the distracted souls we cared for eventually recovered and were able to return to their previous lives – though they were always replaced by others in desperate need. A few simply stayed with us, often relieved of their great torment and able to live their lives whilst under our safe roof, but still in need of care and unable to cope with life outside these walls. It was not at all what I had planned, for I had thought that all our residents could be cured. Yet our experiences quickly taught us much about the proper care of the poor souls who had lost their wits. We now understand which type of lunatick is likely to improve if given the right sort of treatment, but sadly I have to accept that it is not always possible to provide a cure – some are simply too far gone to ever be fully restored to their senses. Still, I am hopeful that, as we become more enlightened in matters of science and medicine, some of the great medics of our time will be able to explain how the disorders of the mind are caused, and thus how we can help those who suffer so. I know I will not see that in my lifetime, so I will leave it to those who follow after me, and we will simply do what we can for now.

My desire for the future is that a lunatick in genuine need will be able to come to the Bethel, and the decision to admit them will be based on their mental condition and the prospect of a cure, and not on their ability to pay. That seems fair, as I have come to believe – to know, in fact – that life has not been fair or kind to a great many of those who suffer such torments. And I hope that in some small way, for some of my lunaticks at least, I can rebalance the scales.

'FOR THE RECEPTION, MAINTENANCE AND CURE OF POOR LUNATICKS'

I am truly an old woman now, and I am living at the Bethel with lunaticks all around me. Our good reputation has grown, and all our rooms are full. The Widow Taylor and Mrs Crick have stayed with us, as has Mr Brightwell, who, like me, is still hanging on. I have appointed Mr Harston's wife as mistress of the House, to oversee the female residents, and we have taken on more attendants. For now, at least, the Bethel seems to run itself.

We also have a new physician, Doctor Theophilus Stringfellow. We were becoming a little demanding of dear Sir Benjamin's time, for he is a busy and important gentleman, though of course he was too kind-hearted to ever refuse our requests for assistance. I reached an agreement with Doctor Stringfellow whereby, in lieu of board for his own brother-in-law, who is staying with us for a while, the good doctor will provide us with medical care for our residents. Doctor Stringfellow has come to us highly recommended and is diligent, though he is a bit of an odd one, with some finickity ways. But he takes his time with the lunaticks and shows an intense interest; he even says that he is more compelled to visit the Bethel than to attend to the fainting fits of the rich, bored wives of the city gentlemen. He is at times a little bit fussy over unimportant details and is a bit of a trial to me, but he is pleasant, and, thus, I try to be patient. He is fastidious in his dress but rather lax with the containment of his personal gases. What is it with men and their noxious noises? How is it that their flatulence seems to please them so? My own dear Samuel was quite an exceptional man, and husband, but even he was not immune. He would at least try to move outside to save my glares, but I could see his amusement at his own untimely squeaks, which he rapidly followed with an innocent look and swift denial. At times, it seems there is not enough lavender in the county to cover the worst of their odours. I do wish men would desist; oh, Lord, perhaps I should add that to my list of House rules.

Despite having the support of my loyal friends, and good staff, I must say it has all been quite exhausting. My mind is continually full of new plans and ideas, for changes or improvements, but my body is slowing. I have to rest more, and I depend on others to carry out tasks that once I would have jumped up to do without any thought. And, of course, every day, many times a day now, I wish that Samuel could have been by my side, to share this with me. I cannot say that my life is hard, not when I see how others suffer, nor is overseeing the running of the Bethel a burden; of course not, it is an honour, but that cannot make my bones ache any less, or stop my heart from missing Samuel so.

I have days when I struggle to get through, unsure if I have the strength to continue. Days when the prospect of lying down and letting the world and all its troubles pass by sorely tempts me, but then, just when I feel I have no more energy left inside, another day begins. I wake and think of Sam, and I look for a while at his boots by the fire, then I carefully swing my legs out of bed and slowly rise. I take a few moments to look out over the garden, and I give thanks to God. The Widow Taylor comes in with a dish of peppermint tea and a piece of plain bread. She fills my washing bowl, adds some rosewater and lays out my clothes for the day. I wash my hands, which have become thin and wrinkled, and I notice my fingers, which are twisted and no longer elegant. Then I rinse my face and tuck the few strands of my hair, which I still refuse to cut, into my cap. My clothes hang off me, for, as I have aged, I have turned to bone, though there is no need for me to waste money on new clothes, and I will make do with what I have. Thus, prepared as best I can, I walk to meet the Widow Taylor who is waiting patiently for me at the top of our staircase, and together we descend, albeit a little cautiously these days, to wherever we are needed.

Most days, I sit by the window to write for as long as my poor, tired eyes will allow. I keep a book in my room, locked in Samuel's old oak chest, and I painstakingly record details of the noteworthy events of the Bethel, and the stories of some of our residents. I have a notion that I may leave this book to the future trustees, so that they may reflect and learn from my experiences, and hence be better able to help the lunaticks who will fill these rooms after I am gone. Or I may just bury it away to protect the stories of those who have played a part in our history thus far. Whichever choice I make, I have taken the trouble to obscure the details of the residents here, as some have been friends or people who were known to others in our great city. I wish to protect their names from the curiosity of future generations, for some still believe that those deprived of their reason bring shame upon their kin.

I look out of my window, where I can see a small group of our residents enjoying a walk in the garden, under the caring eyes of their attendants. I can hear their gentle chatter mixed with the clamour of the streets beyond our walls. There are others, of course, who are not allowed to roam so freely for their own safety, and in our cellar, which I have made as comfortable as possible, there is Ruth, whom sadly we have to keep gently restrained for she is quite deranged now. I visit each lunatick every day to oversee their progress. Some know me now and greet me affectionately; others show no more than a glimmer of recognition; and some throw whatever is close at hand. But I know them all. I can see those we have with us now and I am reminded of the circumstances of those who have left us, my most memorable lunaticks:

CHARITY – ONE OF THE 'GREAT AND THE GOOD'

Charity was the wife of one of the city aldermen. Her husband was an unpleasant man of immense power and influence, both in Norwich and in London, and for her sake I have taken great pains to hide her identity. Charity stayed with us for some time and was one of the first of our true lunaticks, requiring constant care and supervision. I feel I was a little bullied into accepting her, but her husband wished to keep the circumstances of her illness from his fellows and knew he could be assured of our discretion regarding her stay with us. I was disturbed by her appearance for, when she arrived, she had quite lost her senses. She had a deranged look about her and was lacking even the basics of personal care. Her husband had told his friends and colleagues an elaborate tale of her having to leave the city to visit a sick relative, but in truth he simply locked her away, for many months, in his grand house, providing her with plates of food from his own extravagant table but offering no care, kindness or companionship. She had deteriorated so quickly, becoming violent and harming herself and anybody who came close, that he approached me to see if I could offer any treatment. It was clear he could not bear the embarrassment of having her admitted to one of the private hospitals for fear the state of her would become known. Whatever, I had little choice but to admit her. I couldn't turn her away, not in that sorry condition and in such desperate need, and I felt she would certainly benefit from some time apart from her husband. I also knew that he had been opposed to my hospital in the early days, and that he was one of the men who had tried to prevent me from gaining the lease for our piece of waste ground. The Bethel was becoming more widely recognised for the good we were doing, but still I couldn't risk upsetting him, for he had the power to spread untruths about us. Thus, we reached an agreement, unspoken of course, as I had learnt from my father how to negotiate with powerful men.

Charity already looked very different from the person we could recall drifting importantly about the city, in all her jewellery and finery, as she accompanied her husband on his business. Now her hair was filthy and matted, and we had no option but to carefully shave it off. Her clothes were in a loathsome state, and we removed and then burnt them. Dressed in our clean but plain garments, she was already unrecognisable, but we decided to call her Charity in case any of the attendants took to gossiping. Only the Widow Taylor and I knew her true identity, and we ensured that Charity was treated like all the other residents. She was in quite a distracted state of mind for some time, often needing to be restrained, as gently as we could, for her own safety, but eventually we saw a gradual improvement. I think that perhaps she might not have deteriorated so much if she had received our kind care early in her decline, instead of being locked away so cruelly. When she had fully recovered and was fit to return home, I was asked to dress her in one of her fine gowns (and what we eventually worked out to be a good quality wig of natural hair), then put her in a carriage that was to drive towards Cambridge. Once outside the city walls her husband had his own carriage waiting to bring her back to Norwich, looking as if she had, indeed, just returned from caring for her sick relative. How sad that he had to use such deception, but there are still many in this city who would not understand – I wish it were not so, but clearly, I still have much work to do.

I see Charity from time to time, out and about with her husband. She always contrives to avoid me if we pass in the street; perhaps I remind her of the times I had to oversee the attendants as they struggled to contain her during her more violent outbursts. Or perhaps, now that she is fully in control of her senses again, she prefers to forget the desperate soul she once was. Her husband hasn't forgotten, though; he will not acknowledge me in public either, but then he never did. He boasts of his benevolence towards many of our charitable institutions and makes sure people are aware of his generosity. We do not receive any ongoing support from him; however, from time to time, we have a delivery of some essential provision to our gates, with no evidence of who has sent it – though I recognise the driver of the cart.

EDMUND – AN INNOCENT SON

I think it will be useful to record my reason for declining to accept into our care the son of one of the gentlemen of the city. I had not had any direct dealings with this man, though I had heard that he was a steadfast and trustworthy person, who cared well for his family. On hearing that the Bethel was accepting residents, he called on me and explained that he had 'an innocent son' and requested that we accept him for care and treatment. On closer questioning it was evident that this boy, Edmund, had been born with a mental incapacity. He was being kept out of sight, in clean and respectable rooms near to the family home where his father paid for a local woman to watch over him. As Edmund was the first-born son and unfit to inherit either his father's property or title, his father had appealed to the court to allow his second-born son to inherit in Edmund's place. The court had assessed Edmund and, finding him unable to perform simple tasks such as counting to twenty, they agreed to the father's request. Indeed, the boy was unable to even name his father, and the court quoted this as evidence for its decision. Wanting to do the best for his son, his father implored me to accept Edmund into our care, explaining that the boy was not a danger to himself and had never caused harm to any other; he simply needed a place where his condition would be understood. With sorrow, I explained that we were only able to accept those people we believed were capable of a cure, such as those suffering from a temporary absence of their senses. Poor Edmund was unable to dress himself without assistance and would need constant supervision, and I had to decline his admission. I did at least assist in a small way, for, whilst making enquiries about this gentleman and his son, I had heard rumours that the boy was being cruelly treated by his carer, though in such a way as to never show any signs that might be observed. I reported this to his father, who immediately dispensed with the services of the woman. I suggested that he should ask the Mistress Blackthorn, the soldier boy's mother, for I was able to vouch for her character, and she accepted his offer and was pleased to move into new lodgings, where no one knew of her sad loss. I was quite distressed at having to explain our refusal to admit Edmund and I realised that I must be clearer about the principles on which we based our admissions. I set out the distinction between natural-born idiots, those with an innate mental incapacity, and those whom we regard as lunaticks and can restore to their natural senses – and I made this known about the city to avoid any further misunderstandings.

ELIZABETH – WHO DIED AT HER OWN HAND

With a heavy heart, I have recorded the untimely death, at her own hand, of a young girl, Elizabeth. I will set the details of that dreadful morning carefully in my book in order that we may learn from them.

This poor disturbed girl had attempted to take her own life on many occasions before her admission, and Elizabeth's parents had been at their wits ends. Her mother, in particular, was so distraught by her daughter's behaviour that they had become unable to continue to care for her at home. They asked for our help and not only were they able to contribute to her keep but they also provided some much-needed clothing and linens for our poorer residents. Her parents visited regularly and were encouraged that Elizabeth appeared calm and much improved, and we all had great hopes that she would soon be fit for release. She had started to take part in some of our activities, picking and crushing the herbs that we dried for Mrs Crick's kitchen, and she would walk around our little garden with two other patients, who were also improving and preparing to leave. After some weeks of observing Elizabeth's behaviour, we felt sure that, out of all our residents, she would be the soonest to return home.

But it was not to be. I was sitting quietly, early one autumn morning, when the mistress of the House entered my room in a great hurry and reported that poor Elizabeth had hanged herself, in her sleeping room, with her bed sheet tied to a beam. Immediately we gently persuaded our other residents to move downstairs, to keep them away from Elizabeth's room. I instructed the master to make sure the attendants and orderlies did not discuss her tragic death within earshot of the residents, and outwardly at least there was calm. Doctor Stringfellow was called, though there was little he could do. We talked to all the attendants involved in Elizabeth's care, and evidently there had been no indication that one of her 'episodes' was upon her. I am grateful that in the following month, after an enquiry at the court, both coroner and jury were satisfied that no blame should be attached to any person, though I still find it hard to forgive myself for not being able to prevent her untimely death. However, I am a little at a loss to know how this tragedy could have been prevented, as it seems that a determined lunatick may use whatever is at hand, and we can hardly deprive our patients of bedding or watch all of them constantly day and night, or even, God forbid, restrain them all.

My only comfort is that the poor girl's parents do not hold us accountable as they had already seen how determined she could become when the mood was upon her to do herself harm. Her mother even said that she was grateful to us, as she had not been the one to find her daughter's body – for that horrible possibility had haunted her dreams for many years: a little consolation, perhaps. Elizabeth's parents continue to support us, and they still donate clothes. They even visit occasionally. Her mother says she feels some relief in being close to where Elizabeth spent her last days, and I am happy to grant her access to the sanctuary of our garden whenever she needs.

I do have to accept that I cannot help each and every lunatick who enters this hospital. Some are so badly deranged that even the physicians and apothecaries do not know how best to treat them. I was explaining my frustration about the limits of our knowledge to Doctor Wrench, who reassured me that our treatment is much superior to the other private hospitals he visits, where death occurs frequently and often quite distressingly. We talked of his interest in the bathing therapies, for he subscribes to the medical journals, and he was most excited to explain the popular theory that being doused in very hot then very cold water will calm even the most violent of lunaticks. But I will not allow it here, for he admitted, too, that it often takes several attendants to administer the baths, and it causes the condition of some lunaticks to worsen. I am not convinced of its benefits, and I will certainly not have my lunaticks subjected to any more distress than they already suffer. Until science moves on, we shall simply have to continue to offer those physicks that we know are of benefit, and to provide the kindest care we can. I admit, it seems very little, but I remind myself that for some this works well, and we have seen that even the most deranged of minds can sometimes resolve themselves naturally.

HENRY SUTTON – THE 'FURIOUSLY AND DANGEROUSLY MAD'

Soon after Bob, one of the Bethel's first residents, had left, a new law was passed, the Vagrancy Act of 1714, which allows justices of the peace to detain the 'furiously and dangerously mad'. Such persons are now held responsible for any criminal acts, whether they were in or out of their senses at the time, and many are forcibly taken off the streets and incarcerated in the Bridewell. Of course, the Bridewell is a house of correction, and such brutal conditions are of no help to those poor souls whose minds are so disordered that they cannot help their behaviour. Sadly, this Act is being used by the authorities, with a great deal of enthusiasm, as a legal means of rounding up and locking away those who disrupt the peace. One of those who fell afoul of this law was a man called Henry Sutton. This is my record of his admission to the Bethel:

Henry Sutton had once been an ale-man at the Angel, and he was well known to the patrons as a genial and honest man, who had, on at least one occasion, helped deliver my father home after he had been rather excessive in his consumption of their brandy. He was generally a quietly spoken, cheerful man who seemed happy enough with his way of life. Some said he used to drink heavily at times, but, if so, I never saw him the worse for it. Thus, it was with concern that I heard of his decline into a madness so rageous that he had threatened to burn down his neighbour's dwelling, which had understandably put them in fear of their lives. Henry later came to his senses and, on being told of his menacing behaviour (for he had no memory of the event), he apologised profusely. His neighbours, with admirable Christian understanding, accepted that the poor man had become temporarily deprived of his reason, and took no action against him. Several weeks later, however, Henry was once again found raging in the street and threatening any person, and even a somewhat startled stray dog, with grievous violence. Now seen as highly likely to cause public disorder, Henry came to the attention of the authorities, who took the opportunity to remove him from the streets, and he spent some time in the gaol in Norwich Castle. I first heard news of his incarceration when one of his gaolers appeared at our door, asking to speak to me. This man looked ill at ease as I approached him, for there were several lunaticks wandering about in the hallway behind me. He apologised for disturbing me, then quickly stated his reason. In essence, all those many years ago this gaoler had attended the condemned young soldier whom Samuel had tried to comfort in his last days, and he had been struck by Samuel's great humanity. And, though he had not heard of Samuel's passing, he had heard of our new 'madhouse', though he understood it to be run by the Reverend Chapman and not by his aged widow. Once he had overcome his shock at the sight of me, I encouraged him to continue to speak his case, whereby he told of Henry Sutton's plight, locked away with all sorts of villains and rogues. The gaoler, who had experience of bad people, knew that Henry was not one of them, and that he needed care and help, not the daily brutality of life in the city's gaol. Henry's behaviour was still unpredictable, and he would fly into violent rages over the smallest slight. He needed to be kept off the streets and under constant supervision, and the gaoler asked if we could admit Henry to the Bethel. It was a reasonable idea and I sent a note to Doctor Wrench to ask him to visit Henry in the gaol on his next visit to Norwich to assess his suitability. I felt Doctor Wrench might have a little influence in this matter, but even I was somewhat surprised when he turned up at our door, three days later, with Henry in his carriage, accompanied by my earlier visitor and another hefty guard. Doctor Wrench's only comment was that he could not countenance leaving Henry in such a crowded, stinking cell while the legal arrangements were made for his transfer. With all the sway of a respected (and wealthy) member of our community, Doctor Wrench had moved Henry to the Bethel, to be under his personal care while the transfer documents were approved. The courts would not have argued against Sir Benjamin Wrench, and I doubt the City Committee minded, for there was one more space in the gaol and Henry was now our problem.

We were able to move Henry from the carriage into one of our rooms with little fuss. We assigned our more experienced attendants to stay with him constantly, and for many days Henry was quite docile and pleasant. He would nod and acknowledge me as we passed in our little garden. Did he recognise me? I doubt it, for it was many years since he had last seen me, but, still, he was polite and respectful. However, the peace was not to last. One evening, Henry, who had memorised many of Chaucer's *Canterbury Tales*, had been entertaining a small group, lunatics and attendants, with *The Knight's Tale*, when, after being continually interrupted, he exploded into a vicious rage. Two of the attendants moved quickly to prevent him causing grievous harm to a gentle and inoffensive man, who had simply sat next to Henry, listening keenly to his story. We had clearly been taken in by Henry's genial appearance and demeanour. I am very much against the use of restraints, yet in Henry's case we had no option but to secure him, such was the wildness of his fury. Doctor Wrench attended and prescribed a physick that was recommended for soothing the senses, though even that took many doses and many days to work, but eventually his restraints could be removed. Henry has these rages still, all unpredictable, and all over very trivial matters. He is mostly calm now, but, even so, our other residents keep their distance, and for such a man as Henry, who had lived all his life surrounded by people, I expect this causes him much distress. Outwardly, he is quite fit and healthy, and we keep him safe, and I suppose we saved him from a worse future, locked up and forgotten in the gaol, but he is a sad and lonely little figure now, shuffling around the garden, always accompanied by an attendant, never trusted to be alone.

THE DEATH OF ASTIL SMALLBONE

I am forced to make another sad entry in my book, the loss of one of our long-term residents, Astil Smallbone. His was an unexpected death and one that pains me still. This man would usually appear lucid and cheerful, and he had a gentle disposition, though he had a habit of emitting odd noises and yelps, at random, even in the midst of a quite sensible conversation. We had simply become used to him and I instructed the attendants to ignore this behaviour whenever it occurred. My only concern was that he would, on occasion, curse and use horrible oaths, though he seemed to have little control over this. I may have been born a gentlewoman, but I had heard virtually every oath that could be uttered, often while visiting Samuel's parishioners, particularly some of the old sailors from Yarmouth who had settled in Thorpe in their later years. I had even attended one of Samuel's most respectable church ladies, and she, who had only uttered a quiet, 'well, excuse me…' when a great carthorse splattered her with mud as it clumped by, ended her days cursing fit to scare the Devil.

I pause in my writing, for that memory makes me smile. Oh, my Lord, I hope that does not happen to me – what would people say, the gentle and pious Mary Chapman swearing like a fishwife? Oh, my dear Sam would have laughed till he cried at that thought, but… anyway… I must not get distracted again, for I need to continue with my report. Thus, out of concern for my more delicate ladies, I instructed that Mr Smallbone should be seated slightly away from the other residents at meal-times, when the general hubbub usually disguised his outbursts. I also made sure that he was occupied outside if we had visitors to the hospital, for his rather lively choice of words could sometimes be a little off-putting. I recall one afternoon, whilst I was discussing our exemplary standards of care and supervision with the son of a possible new resident, when Mr Smallbone sauntered into the hallway, swore animatedly at a chair and turned with a great show of dignity and left. I ignored this disturbance and simply carried on talking, though I caught the eye of our visitor, who appeared to be amused, whether by the antics of Mr Smallbone or our gentle tolerance of his behaviour I do not know. Thankfully, it did not put them off, for the visitor's father was admitted shortly afterwards.

When Mr Smallbone first arrived he would rarely speak, confining himself to his room and refusing to venture even to the window. After a while, though, his attendants observed him peering outside, for a sight of a small corner of the garden. The Widow Taylor had the idea of moving him to a room that looked out over the whole garden, though when we went in and explained our idea to him he looked blankly at us then turned his back. A little defeated, we left him alone, though we were not halfway down the corridor when he chased after us, his few possessions bundled into his arms. Once we moved his room, and he could see all the goings-on, he was tempted to venture outside, and thence he spent every possible minute in the garden, happily doing tasks as instructed by Mr Brightwell. I had begun to think that we could offer Mr Smallbone a permanent place, perhaps as a gardener's assistant. I knew he had no family to return to, and also that others outside these walls may not have been as tolerant of his swearing and odd ways as we were. He certainly loved our little garden and would always keep himself busy, tidying here and there, long after Mr Brightwell had retired to Mrs Crick's kitchen. The orderlies had quite a task trying to persuade him to retire to his room even when the weather was cold and the nights were drawing in, and, sadly, his love of being outside probably contributed to his death.

It was reported to me, too late as it turned out, that Mr Smallbone had slipped whilst sweeping the leaves from the paths around the flower beds. The attendants, who were warming themselves by the fire rushed outside upon hearing his cries, and he was conveyed to bed. Sadly, poor Mr Smallbone had banged his head on the hard ground but the fracture to his skull was not discovered until the following evening, when Mr Harston examined him more closely. Medical assistance from Mr Stringfellow was immediately procured but by then it had been a full twenty-six hours since the fall, and Mr Smallbone died soon after. I sat with him for that time, knowing he had no kin, to ensure that at least he would not be alone in his final hours, as I feel we had let him down whilst he was under our care. On later examination and based on the evidence from Doctor Stringfellow, an enquiry by the court concluded that Mr Smallbone's death was the inevitable consequence of his fall, and not of the unhappy delay in seeking treatment. Therefore, none of the attendants were dismissed, though I reminded them all of the requirement that any accident should be reported immediately to Mr Harston directly, or to myself in his absence.

WILLIAM WINTER AND HIS WILY WITS

The next entry in my book records the events of the fourteenth day of April, when one of our newest patients, a wandering lunatick by the name of William Winter, made his escape over the wall and has not been heard of since. His escape caused much consternation amongst our residents. He was first spotted by two of our older ladies who were contentedly struggling around the garden together, both talking nonsense, though, thankfully, neither of them realising. They started shrieking and waving their walking sticks as they observed Mr Winter sitting atop our boundary wall, a leg either side, almost hidden amongst the branches of the apple tree – a place that was quite cunningly chosen by him, I feel. It turned out, as reported by the attendant who was helping the ladies prepare for bed later, while listening to them excitedly retelling the story, that they had thought a man was breaking *into* the garden, and they didn't like the look of that at all.

As this man made his escape, all at once there were attendants, Mr Brightwell and Mrs Crick and her kitchen maids, coming from all directions and running towards the wall. Thus unsupervised, some of the lunaticks took the opportunity to make the most of their freedom and chased about the garden, doing a great deal of damage to my beautiful flower beds, while others simply wandered back to the House, unconcerned by the commotion. At one point in amongst the chaos I had cause to shout at the top of my voice to restore order. It shocked everybody present – it certainly shocked me. I did not realise I had such a loud voice, having never had cause to shout before. Thankfully, no one was hurt, and we eventually managed to calm everyone, and all of our remaining lunaticks were accounted for. The master and two attendants went to search the streets of Norwich for our escapee, even going beyond the city wall, but, perhaps not surprisingly, there were no sightings of the wily Mr Winter.

Once all the fuss was over, we had discussions with our attendants to make it clear that, should something so exciting ever happen again, they must remain with the lunatick under their care, to prevent further disruption or damage being done, and they must let those nearest the trouble deal with the incident. Needless to say, I instructed Mr Brightwell to prune the overhanging branches from the apple tree, without delay.

Mr Winter was perhaps a strange case. Although appearing to exhibit lunatick behaviour, two of our orderlies had reported seeing him act in a most normal manner at times, that is, until the master or one of the attendants passed by, when once again he would begin his strange twitching. Following his disappearance, I now suspect that this man just needed a place to stay while he was passing through Norwich and thought he could fake madness and so benefit from our generosity. I rather feel that the reality of life inside our hospital, though of a much kinder nature than many other asylums, is still not an easy place to reside, so perhaps he had had enough and decided to take his chance and seek lodgings elsewhere. I am a little cross that we were fooled in this way, for we have little enough space here and his room could have been used to help another person in his stead. In any case, Mr Winter and his wily wits have taught us much and we will learn from this episode. Henceforth, we will be more aware that certain disreputable persons may desire to 'fake' their lunacy, for whatever reason. And, as some of our genuine lunaticks may also share his cunning, I have instructed the master to ensure that all ladders and benches are moved away from the walls to foil any further attempts by any of our residents to leave without our authority.

ERASMUS QUANTRELL – NO BLAME ATTACHED

I confess I am shaking as I write my final report. On Thursday last, one of our more disturbed residents, Erasmus Quantrell, attempted to commit suicide, during supper, by cutting his own throat. One of the attendants who was supervising the meal-time managed to wrest the knife from his hand, with great courage, and the master was able to stop the flow of blood until Doctor Stringfellow arrived and was able to expertly bind the wound of poor Mr Quantrell. There was an enormous confusion in the dining room and much distress was caused to even our calmest residents. We are currently using the lunaticks' day room for serving meals, as some of our residents are refusing to even enter the room where this incident occurred, despite the orderlies taking great care to mop all his blood from the tiled floor. I have instructed Mr Brightwell to burn the small dining table, which still shows some bloodstains, to fully erase any reminders of that dreadful day.

Doctor Stringfellow has been attending daily and we fully expected Mr Quantrell to recover. The apothecary provided a calming physick and we nursed him with small sips of broth and herbal teas. However, despite our best efforts over the past few days, the gaping wound failed to heal and, indeed, Mr Quantrell was able to pull the wound apart again, so determined was he to die, and I am sad to report that this evening we were unable to save him. No blame has been attached to anyone as we believe that the attendants supervising supper-time could not have predicted his behaviour as it was so out of character. In recognition of Doctor Stringfellow's excellent care of Mr Quantrell, and our other residents, I have just written a letter offering him the position as our permanent physician, which I am confident he will accept, for it is likely that his brother-in-law will be with us for some time.

HAPPIER TIMES

I pause, and then, at the very bottom of the page, I write my final words, *Per ardua stabilis*. I lay down my quill and let my memory drift to happier times.

I am blessed to have met many generous and kindly people throughout my life – those who have tried to make this brutal life a little more bearable for those who have no choice but to struggle through. I pray I get the chance to thank my dear friends who have helped and supported me, for I would not have achieved all this without them, and I give thanks for the patience of those to whom I have possibly been a bit of a nuisance, over the years. I have recorded, in this book, alongside the stories of my lunaticks, the names of the people to whom I owe a great debt, in the hope that those who come after us will recognise the part they played in the life of the Bethel.

Of course, there have been people, even in our benevolent city, who have wished me ill, wanting to see the Bethel fail and close – those who consider that lunaticks should be locked away, out of sight – but I will not waste my time thinking of them, the poor of spirit, for I will simply let them answer to God when their time comes.

I think again of one of the kindest men I have known, the eminent Sir Benjamin, who has of late been indisposed with gout. My dear Doctor Wrench has succumbed to that disease of rich men, despite my admonishments to curtail his intake of the game that he loves so well, and to cut down on the buttery sauces a little. Though I should like to add here that I am grateful to Doctor Wrench for his kind attention, and for his dedication and skill. As such, I had written to him to express my great sense of the benefits that this Institution has derived from his valuable services, and to thank him for his friendship. I also gave him a tincture of crocus, as recommended by Culpeper, and a bottle of my elderflower cordial, which I suggested he should take with meals as an alternative to his fortified wines. He laughed when he saw it, holding it at arm's length, pretending that he thought it was a bottle of cow's urine, an old remedy for gout. Well, as I sternly informed him, I could arrange that too, but until then perhaps he would humour me and use the cordial, for I was certain it would do him much good. I acknowledged that he may not enjoy it quite as much as his expensive wines.

MY BELOVED LUNATICKS

It makes me smile to think of the great Sir Benjamin Wrench. I am honoured to have known him, though I am certain he will tip my tincture away, then tell me, quite guilelessly, how beneficial he found it, when we next converse. I smile, too, when I think of how he used to sit with me and my ladies in my summer rose garden, getting them all into a bit of a flutter by his mere presence – how he would stretch out his long legs, turn his face to the sun and listen to their chatter, occasionally opening an eye to look at me when one of their inopportune comments amused him. Many years back he had come across Ellen and me in my rose garden, surrounded by some of the gentler lady lunaticks, who had taken it upon themselves to join us, quite uninvited. I had intended to keep a section of the rose garden as my own private space, but we had been enlivened by the company of those ladies, for there was a joy in their kind of madness. The lunaticks changed over the years, some leaving and a few returning, but those sunny scented afternoons turned into some of my happiest times at the Bethel. Benjamin Wrench had refrained from commenting when he had first come across our little group, but from thenceforth he referred to us as the 'Mary Chapman Club'. I have, more than once, just wanted to tuck myself under his arm and hug him, for the bigness of his heart, though, of course, Mary Chapman, widow, would not do such a thing – but I hope he knows how important he has been to me, and to this place.

I am sitting as the evening draws to a close, remembering my life here at the Bethel, recorded for all time, in my book. There are some sad stories contained in its pages, but there are hopeful tales, too, of the lunaticks we have been able to cure and return to their grateful families, to live out their lives. And those who have died of natural causes here? Well, I sat with them so that, however cruel their life had been, they would at least find comfort at the end – they did not pass from this life alone.

And thus, I ask myself if I have achieved my aim, as it is written above the entrance to this hospital: 'To do good, and to share with others'. The Bethel is full, but there are still too many poor disturbed souls on our streets, in the gaol and in the Bridewell, who continue to suffer the most brutal of lives, and I find I cannot answer. So, I will leave it up to God to judge me too.

I climbed the stairs very slowly tonight, pausing to remind a passing house-maid to freshen the flowers in the entrance hall, before waving the Widow Taylor away with a smile, thanking her for her kindness towards me, but wanting some time in my room, alone, to make sure all is in order. I take off my widow's black, then dress myself in my deep green taffeta, struggling to wrap the heavy material about my withered body. I take off my cap and remove the pins to let my hair fall loose. I have already dusted and organised Samuel's books, and his boots are in their place by the fire. I go to Samuel's oak chest and bury my book, the story of the Bethel, deep amongst his clothes, convinced that I can still smell the scent of the crumbling rose petals that are scattered there. I run my hand over the smooth, shiny surface as I turn the key. Locked and secure, I now leave the contents of his chest for those who come after me.

Next, from the back of my chair, I take my old shawl. Made a lifetime ago by my father, and once a rich dark green shot through with threads of gold, it is now faded and fine, after years of giving comfort. I inhale as I hold it close to my face, believing for a second that I am breathing in the years of my childhood. I wrap the key to Samuel's chest and the engraving of my Lord in its silver frame, in that piece of worn-out cloth, then slip them into a gap in the wood underneath my window. A part of me that will stay to watch over this place – for ever after.

I write an inscription in some of the books from Samuel's study, now piled on my side table, with instructions on how they are to be distributed, as small tokens of my gratitude, for those who have helped me. Then I take my last will out of my cabinet – I plan to take a final look through it tomorrow, when the light is better, just for my own peace of mind, though in truth I am satisfied that it contains my exact instructions for how this hospital is to be run after my death.

I glance out of the window and see, once again, in the shadows of the wall, one of our laundry-maids in a close embrace with one of the male attendants; they are both young, both full of desire. I had disturbed them earlier this evening, as I walked slowly and painfully around my rose garden at dusk. They had moved away from each other, chastened, when they saw me, but I did not admonish them; I gave them a small smile and wished them a good evening. They must have noticed that my steps were faltering for they came after me and guided me inside, to a chair at the bottom of the staircase, where I said I would sit for a while. I thanked them for their thoughtfulness and reassured them that I was quite well, so they took their leave and returned to their sheltered spot by the wall. In that moment, I remembered my loves and my losses, and I suddenly wanted to call them back, to urge them to live life without regret, and to seek passion throughout their lives. To tell them that they too may grow old, and they may lose those who now love them so. But I did not speak, for they are young, and they will live, and they will learn.

Now, looking around my room, I have a sudden desire to gather around me my most precious possessions. I am reminded of the woman I once was, with Samuel, so complete, so loved. I go to the bottom drawer of my cabinet and stoop to lift out the bodice from my wedding dress. I carefully unwrap it and a few pieces of ancient, dried rose soap fall to the floor. I hold the bodice close and remember how Samuel had held me and slowly traced the flowers and the vines with his finger, when at last we had been left alone on our wedding night.

I am taken back to my early years, when I simply wanted to serve God, to care for my kin and to do good in my life, and, later, how I wanted also to love and to live with passion.

And yes, though I sit here, with my bony frame hidden in my deep green gown and looking like the dried-up old maid I had always feared I would become, I am suddenly completely content and at peace. I know that my dour appearance does not tell the whole story. Let those who know me remember me, and perhaps tell others. All I wish is that my Bethel, Samuel's Bethel, will endure, for ever after, and give comfort to such persons as are deprived of their reason and understanding. My beloved lunaticks.

Twelve

'IT IS MY WILL AND MIND'

EXCERPTS FROM THE WILL OF MARY CHAPMAN

In the Name of God, Amen, the fourth day of December, in the fourth year of the reign of our Sovereign Lord George, by the grace of God... King, Defender of the Faith, and in the year of our Lord God, one thousand seven hundred and seventeen, I, Mary Chapman, of the City of Norwich, widow, and relict of that truly eminent, pious and faithful servant of God and Minister of the Gospel of our Lord and Saviour Jesus Christ, Samuel Chapman, late of Thorpe next Norwich, Clerk, deceased; being of a sound and disposing mind and memory (Praised be God for it) do hereby revoke and make void all former wills by me made, and make this my last Will and Testament...

First, and before all things, I humbly dedicate and most heartily devote to God myself, Soul, Body and Spirit... with all I am and to whom I owe my being and well-being. (My Soul hath said unto the Lord thou art my Portion, therefore will I hope in Thee.)

The Lord is the portion of my Cup. It is He that maintaineth my lot. I have steadfastly resolved to keep myself in the Love of God, looking for the mercies of our Lord Jesus Christ unto Eternal Life. Now, unto Him Who is able to keep from falling and to present me faultless before the presence of His Glory with exceeding joy; to the only wise God our Saviour be Glory, Majesty, Dominion, and Power, both now and forever, Amen.

FROM THE LAST WILL AND TESTAMENT OF MARY CHAPMAN

I nominate, appoint and make William Cockman sole Executor of this my last Will and Testament and I do give unto him twenty pounds for his pains to be taken in and about the execution of this my will.

I give twenty shillings to be divided and distributed by my Executor among the poor widows of the parish where I shall die, and twenty shillings to the poor widows of Thorpe-next-Norwich.

I will and devise unto my worthy and faithful friends, of the said City of Norwich, John Hall, and William Cockman, citizens and aldermen, and to Richard Cooke, gentleman, John Lombe, worsted weaver, John Thompson, darnick weaver, William Lombe, merchant, and Timothy Ganning, upholsterer, of the said City… and to their heirs for ever… all my messuages, lands, tenements and hereditaments.

And that they shall, out of the rents, issues or profits from the sale of the above, discharge the sum of thirty pounds per annum to Hannah, currently the wife of Francis Keeling, formerly the wife of my late brother Robert Mann, deceased.

I will that the rest and the residue of the rents issued, and profits thereof shall be used that this Charity may be continued and established for ever.

My will is that on my death… the said House of Bethel shall be an independent Trust, Charity or Foundation, managed by committee of the aforementioned seven Trustees, and regulated by specific instructions laid out in my will.

My will and mind is that all my ready money and securities for money, chattels, and personal Estate, whatsoever shall remain in the hands of my Executor, to be by him improved the best he honestly and fairly can until he and my other Trustees judge it to be sufficient to go on with and proceed with the creation and running of this charitable Trust.

THE SUM OF TWENTY SHILLINGS

I give unto every one of my said Trustees which shall be living at the time of my death twenty shillings a piece to buy them a ring.

And I will and devise to each and every of my said Trustees and their successors the sum of twenty shillings a piece each year, and every year towards necessary expenses, in and about the execution of this Trust. If their necessary expenses are higher, they shall pay themselves what they shall judge reasonable over and above the twenty shillings a piece for the first five years and no more.

THE LOCKED BOX

And I will that the said Trustees shall buy a convenient box… wherein the writings and evidences and other things relating to the said Charity shall be put and secured. That the box shall be always kept in some safe part of the House, or in the house of one of the Trustees. There should be at least four very good locks of a different sort or make, and that each lock shall have two keys; one for each lock will be held by one of the Trustees and the other key to each lock will be stored in the box. Not any one of the Trustees or their successors will be able to open the box alone. If one of the Trustees should die, the key will be passed to their successor.

And it is my further will and mind that my said Trustees shall also buy a book wherein shall be written and kept, all the proceedings relating to the running of the Trust. This book shall be put and secured among the other writings and evidence in the box.

FOR THE POOR LUNATICKS

And it is my further will and mind that five pounds per annum shall be yearly and every year lay'd out for necessary shirts, shifts and other clothing for such poor lunatick persons as shall be in the said House, at the discretion and by the direction of my said Trustees.

THE MASTER

It is my will that two chaldron of coal shall be yearly and every year allowed to the Master or Governor of the said House.

THAT THIS CHARITY MAY CONTINUE FOREVER

And further my will and mind is that if any of my said Trustees shall leave the City of Norwich or be absent for six months, despite a summons to attend Trust meetings, a replacement will be appointed by the remaining Trustees. And this method shall continue for ever and such person or persons to be chosen hereafter will have the same power given to the original Trustees.

It is my will that no person appointed as Trustee shall be able to make over their Trust to the Court of Mayoralty of the City of Norwich. And that this Charity shall never come into the hands of the said Court and that neither they nor any of them acting as a public society shall be any way concerned in the execution of this Trust.

And that this Charity may be continued and established for ever, I will that when one of my said Trustees shall die or depart this life, the survivors or the major part of them shall within three months next after his death nominate, appoint or choose by a writing under their hands some other honest and credible person who shall be joined to them.

I will that these scriptures following shall be recorded upon some stone or plank and placed within the said House, where my Trustees shall think best, (that is to say):

Let not the wise man glory in his wisdom
Jeremiah, 9th chapter, 23rd verse

Who maketh thee to differ from another
Corinthians, 4th chapter, 7th verse

Surely oppression maketh a wise man mad
Ecclesiastes, 7th chapter, 7th verse

The Lord is God of knowledge and by Him actions are weighed
Samuel, 2nd chapter, 3rd verse

Thirteen

'I WISH MY BODY TO BE LAID IN A PLAIN COFFIN'

MARY, EIGHTH DAY OF JANUARY 1724

Night has fallen, the Bethel is peaceful, and I know I am dying. I am seventy-six years old and I am filled with joy.

I have survived my husband by nearly a quarter of a century, and I miss him. I am tired of all the suffering I have seen, and with God's grace I am ready to join my dearest Samuel at last. He whom I loved.

I know there is a place that has been held for me, next to my beloved Sam, in the soft earth inside the chancel of his church, and I take comfort that we will rest, side by side, for all time. I pray that he would approve of my fortitude in surviving this long without him, and of my endeavours in achieving our aim, our Bethel.

I have created this House, this legacy, this place of care. My will contains my wishes for the disposal of my estate wherewith it pleased God to bless me. My great desire is that my trustees will stay true to their word and create a charitable trust in order that the Bethel Hospital may be established for ever – and that it may continue to do good.

Day by day now I have sensed my final decline. I have just summoned the last remnants of my strength and moved painfully to the window to look out onto my garden, frost-covered and bare. I cannot see any of my lunaticks, though I know they will be safe and warm inside. I think I hear a knock at the door and a baby cry but perhaps my sound and disposing mind is letting go at last. I return to sit, as upright as I can, on my straight-backed chair, the very chair I have retired to for the past eleven years, after I have welcomed lunaticks, their families, and a whole variety of benefactors and medical men, and my true friends, to this place, this House, my home, our Bethel.

I am determined that I will be remembered for my strength during my life, not my sad decline as I reach the end of my days. It appears that I am so successful some are persuaded that I may yet recover from this most recent bout of ill health, but I am not fooled; each day it takes more effort to hold myself in place, when truly I wish I could perhaps just slip away with the minimum of fuss. I imagine my body could gently crumble, unnoticed, and be absorbed into this building, my presence here for ever, protecting those who wish to do good, and as a warning to those who might wish to do this place harm.

But it seems it all takes time.

I can see my hands, fading now against the rich greenness of my dress, but I know they are resting on my most precious possession, Samuel's worn and well-read, and loved, volume of *The Pilgrim's Progress from This World to That Which Is to Come.* I feel it is a rather fitting title as I slowly, painfully, make my own progress towards the world which is to come. Sam's book is the one possession I have taken to keeping with me at all times so that I can be sure I am holding it close to me in my last moments on this earth – the book that Samuel most treasured and read from every day but which I have been unable to open since his death. Those final lines, the ones I softly said to him so that he might be comforted as he fell into a sleep that brought an eternal night, I say them now:

> *They therefore went up through the regions of the air, sweetly talking as they went; being comforted, because they safely got*

over the river, and had such glorious companions to attend them...

I must drift off for when I wake the room around me has faded. I can feel the book in my hands, loosely now, but I know it is there. And I say the words again,

... up through the regions of the air... sweetly talking... comforted... glorious companions...

and again,

... up... through... the air... comforted...

My gift to him. He who made me. He whom I loved.

His book is with me now.

He is with me now.

And I look down at my long elegant fingers.

'I wish my body to be laid in a plain coffin'

My Body, I commit to the earth to be decently buried in the chancel of the Parish Church of Thorpe, as near as conveniently may be to the body of my most eminent, pious and faithful servant of God, my husband Samuel Chapman, deceased, without giving any disturbance thereto...

... and my will and mind is that my funeral shall be as private and with as little ceremony as decently may be...

... and that my body shall be laid in a plain coffin, not lined within or without, and not having any ornaments upon it, only two letters, M.C.

... and that my coffin shall be carried to the grave by six parish clerks, whom my Executor shall think fit and that there be no second bearers, escutcheons, nor velvet pall...

I humbly dedicate and most heartily devote to God myself, Soul, Body and Spirit.

And all that I am.

The graves of Mary and Samuel Chapman

Fourteen

'THAT THIS WOMAN HATH DONE WILL BE TOLD FOR A MEMORIAL OF HER'

Under this stone resteth in hopes of a joyful resurrection
the body of that exemplary, pious and charitable widow
Mrs. MARY CHAPMAN,
daughter of John Man, esq.,
Mayor of Norwich and High Sheriff of Norfolk,
and relict of the Rev. Mr SAM CHAPMAN,
formerly rector of this church.
She built wholly at her own expense
the House in Norwich called Bethel,
for the reception, maintenance and cure of poor lunaticks,
to which and other charitable uses
she gave all her incomes while she lived and her estate at her death,
which happened on
the 8th day of January in the year of our Lord, 1724
and of her age the 76th

That this woman hath done will be told for a memorial of her
Math. XXVI, 13

Mary Chapman was buried next to her husband in the chancel of their parish church, by the river at Thorpe-next-Norwich. The tiny church became too small for the increasing population of Thorpe, and in the 1860s a huge new St Andrews Church was built. In the 1880s the old church was ruinated, and hence Samuel and Mary's graves now appear to be outside, though they were both originally buried inside the church.

On 13th December 1897, at a meeting of the trustees of the Bethel, it was noted that a grateful patient, who had received much Christian kindness from the officials and nurses at the Bethel, after 'experiencing cruelties and persecutions in five different Asylums', wished the tombstone of the foundress to be renovated. The original inscription over her tomb, defaced by exposure to the weather in the ruined and roofless chancel, had become unreadable. The inscription was cut onto a new marble stone and the letters filled in with lead. This was done at the governors' expense.

Mary's Bethel Hospital continued to care for people with mental health conditions for more than 280 years, until it was finally closed in 1995. While it did not quite endure for ever, as she wished, this remarkable woman still left an extraordinary legacy.

THE TRUE STORY OF MARY CHAPMAN AND THE BETHEL HOSPITAL

Although based on real people and true events, this is a work of fiction.

Using dates and descriptions of actual events that occurred both in Norwich, and nationally, during Mary's lifetime, and including as many facts about Mary and the people in her life as I could find, this book is otherwise my imaginings of how a woman born into those times might succeed in creating such a monument to perseverance and goodness.

I was able to gain some insight into Mary's life and her character from her very lengthy will, reproduced in part in this novel. Her words reflect her love for her husband, Samuel, her faith in God, and a desire to do good for the 'poor lunaticks' in Norwich.

My main source of inspiration and information was *The History of the Bethel Hospital at Norwich, Built by Mrs Mary Chapman in 1713*, published in 1906. It was written by Sir Frederick Bateman and completed, after his death, by Walter Rye, both trustees of the Bethel. It includes the building agreement in full, Mary's will of 1717, a long account of the Great Blowe, and Benjamin Wrench's letter. It also has detailed accounts of the organisation and management of the Bethel as a charitable trust after Mary's death, and transcriptions of some of the meetings of the trustees from 1724 to 1905.

Mary Mann was born in 1647, the daughter of John Mann, alderman, sheriff and mayor of Norwich. She did not marry until she was thirty-five, when she became the second wife of the Reverend Samuel Chapman, rector of Thorpe. Walter Rye, writing in about 1903, has suggested that both Mary and Samuel had family who suffered from mental illness, although he did not identify which members of their families might have been so afflicted. He stated, 'It might be possible to trace out who they were, but I think it better to leave this part alone.' I have followed his example, and Ellen is Mary's fictional sister.

Mary and Samuel were together until Samuel's death in 1700, when Mary was fifty-three; there were no children from the marriage. Samuel bequeathed to Mary, in his will, money to build 'a hospital for the habitation of poor lunaticks'.

On 12th December 1712, Mary's 'trusted and faithful' friends signed, on her behalf, a 1,000-year lease on a piece of land, the former site of the Committee House, which had been flattened in the Great Blowe of 1648. The Bethel was completed in 1713 and Mary lived there until her death in 1724. I have assumed that the Bethel was run as a private hospital until Mary's death, as there are no records for this period.

Sir Benjamin Wrench, Hannah, the Widow Taylor, the trustees and Mary's 'worthy and faithful friends' were all real people who played a significant part in Mary's life. Some of the 'memorable lunaticks' are based on descriptions taken from Bateman and Rye's book, although from the period after Mary's death, and names have been changed.

SIR BENJAMIN WRENCH

Sir Benjamin Wrench was appointed first physician to the House. After serving for twenty-two years, he sent the following letter to the trustees, read at the meeting of the trustees on 12th January 1746:

Gentlemen,

The season of the year and my own advanced age rendering it difficult for me to visit the Bethel, as usual; and having now fully performed my promise to Mrs Chapman in attending as Physician, so long as I was able, I send this to desire you to provide some other person proper to succeed me; and till then I shall readily give my assistance upon any occasion that may require it.

I am, Gentlemen,
Your most obliged and humble servant
BENJAMIN WRENCH.

Benjamin Wrench remained a trustee until his death in 1747. It was noted in the Charity Commissioners' Report of 1833, that he, 'from time to time remitted his salary, which amounted in the whole to £352'.

GLOSSARY

Alderman
A member of an English county or borough council, next in status to the mayor. A man of high rank.

Apprentices
An apprentice was bound to a master whilst learning a trade, usually for a fixed term of seven years. Apprentices were not permitted to marry.

Bandolier
Shoulder belt for ammunition.

Bell-man
A town crier.

Calicoes
Fine muslins, often printed and imported from Bengal, and seen as a threat to the home-spun fabrics.

Chaldron
A chaldron or chauldron was an English measure of dry volume, commonly used for coal. In 1694 it was defined by law as fifty-three long hundredweight (5940 lbs, 2690 kg).

Chattels
Personal property.

Darnick weaver

Darnick/dornix was a type of coarse wool and linen cloth which originated in the Dutch town of Doornijk.

Escutcheons

A flat, decorative piece of metal often screwed to a coffin lid and used as a guide for the thumbscrew.

Freedom of the City

Being 'accepted to the Freedom of the City' gave the right to trade. It was only bestowed on members of a guild or livery, who were known as 'freemen'.

Gardiner's mare

Quoted by Blomefield in his description of the Great Blowe as meaning 'the gallows'.

Gewgaws, geegaws

A showy bauble or trinket that attracts attention but has no value or use.

Gimmer (double-jointed)

A hinge.

Godly men

Puritans. They rarely referred to themselves as 'Puritans' as this was a pejorative term.

Guild

An association of artisans, craftsmen or merchants who controlled the practice of their craft in their town. Guild Halls are a legacy of traditional guilds, constructed and used as meeting places. Each individual guild generally recognised three ranks of workers: apprentices, journeymen and masters.

Haire morter
Mortar with the addition of animal hair, horse, cow or goat to increase its strength.

Hereditaments
An item of property that can be inherited (land, building or rents on a property).

Journeyman
A skilled worker who had successfully completed an apprenticeship in a building trade or craft. They were considered competent and authorised to work in that field as a fully qualified employee.

Lady Day
In England, Lady Day was the start of the new year, between 1155 and 1752. It is the traditional name of the Feast of the Annunciation, on 25th March, and refers to Our Lady, the Virgin Mary.

Larth
Used with mortar for plastering internal walls. A larth (lath) is a narrow strip of wood, usually hand-made, which is nailed horizontally to each stud in the frame of an interior wall. Each lath is spaced about a quarter of an inch away from the next so that the mortar can push through.

Lunatick/lunatic
A commonly used term in the seventeenth century. The original meaning was to have the imagination influenced by the moon.

Messuages
A dwelling house, outbuildings and lands.

Master
A master craftsman or master tradesman was a member of a guild. An aspiring master would have to pass through the career chain from apprentice to journeyman before he could be elected to become a master craftsman. He would then have to produce a sum of money and a masterpiece before he could join the guild.

Michaelmas
The feast of St Michael, 29th September.

Muster roll
An inventory or roster. Specifically, it was a register of men, usually of officers and men in a military unit.

Norfolk dumpling
A flour dumpling placed on top of a stew. It is also an old affectionate term for a plump person and/or a country bumpkin.

Physick
Medicinal drugs, prescribed by a physician, and made up by an apothecary. A physick garden contained plants for healing or medicinal purposes.

Pious
Meaning deeply religious. Also meaning devout, devoted, reverent, God-fearing.

Plough Monday
Plough Monday, generally the sixth day of January, was the traditional start of the agricultural year in England, which saw the resumption of work after the Christmas period. The custom was observed particularly in northern and eastern England, whereby a plough was hauled from house to house in a procession, collecting money. They were often accompanied by musicians, an old woman

or a boy dressed as an old woman, called the 'Bessy', and a man in the role of the 'fool'. Plough pudding was a boiled suet pudding, containing meat and onions, and was eaten on Plough Monday, particularly in Norfolk.

Pounds, shillings and pence

After the Norman Conquest in 1066 the pound was divided into twenty shillings or 240 pennies. It remained so until decimalisation on 15th February 1971, when the pound was divided up as it is still done today.

Before 1971 money was divided into:

- pounds (£ or l)
- shillings (s. or /-) and
- pennies (d.)

Quarrell glass

A diamond-shaped piece of glass. Named after the instrument, a glazier's diamond, which is used to cut a piece of glass into a pane by a glazier.

Quo warranto

A legal proceeding during which an individual's right to hold an office or governmental privilege is challenged. In old English practice, the writ of *quo warranto,* an order issued by authority of the king, was one of the most ancient and important writs.

Regalia

The distinctive clothing worn, and ornaments carried, at formal occasions as an indication of status.

Relict

A widow.

Round

A song for three or more voices, each singing the same theme but starting one after another.

Shout

A call to arms.

Smallpox

A viral infection producing fever and a skin rash followed by pustules which left permanent scars. The disease was often fatal until the eighteenth century but is now believed to have been eradicated by vaccination programmes, pioneered by Edward Jenner.

Sneck

Latch on a door or window. 'By the sneck' is taken to mean as the door is finally closed when the building work is complete.

Spangles

Sequins.

Strangers

'Strangers' were Protestant refugees from the Netherlands, then a colony of Catholic Spain, who came to Norwich in the 1560s to escape persecution. By 1579, about 6,000 people (over a third of the population of Norwich) were Strangers. Many were weavers. They looked after their own poor, cared for their sick and worshipped in their own churches.

Ward

An area of the city for which an alderman takes responsibility.

Worsted weaver

Worsted was a fine, smooth cloth spun from the combed long wool of sheep. The term originated from Worsted, a parish in Norfolk, where much of the cloth was woven.

POETRY AND QUOTES

Pages 24, 62
Life is a pure flame, and we live by an invisible sun within us…
From: *Urne Burial*, Thomas Browne

Page 51
How strongly does my passion flow… I languish, sigh, and die.
From: *On Loving Two Equally*, Aphra Benn

Page 54
Love's not Time's fool, though rosy lips and cheeks
Within his bending sickle's compass come:
Love alters not with his brief hours and weeks,
But bears it out even to the edge of doom.
Sonnet 116, William Shakespeare

Pages 58, 67, 91
I wonder, by my troth, what thou and I
Did, till we loved? Were we not weaned till then?
But sucked on country pleasures, childishly?
Or snorted we in the Seven Sleepers' den?
'Twas so; but this, all pleasures fancies be.

If ever any beauty I did see,
Which I desired, and got, 'twas but a dream of thee
And now good-morrow to our waking souls,
Which watch not one another out of fear;
For love, all love of other sights controls,
And makes one little room an everywhere.

Let sea-discoverers to new worlds have gone,
Let maps to other, worlds on worlds have shown,
Let us possess one world, each hath one, and is one.
My face in thine eye, thine in mine appears,
And true plain hearts do in the faces rest;
Where can we find two better hemispheres,
Without sharp north, without declining west?

Whatever dies, was not mixed equally;
If our two loves be one, or, thou and I
Love so alike, that none do slacken, none can die.

The Good-Morrow, John Donne

Page 90
Mark but this flea, and mark in this,
How little that which thou deniest me is;
It suck'd me first, and now sucks thee,
And in this flea our two bloods mingled be.
Thou know'st that this cannot be said
A sin, nor shame, nor loss of maidenhead;
Yet this enjoys before it woo,
And pamper'd swells with one blood made of two;
And this, alas! is more than we would do.

O stay, three lives in one flea spare,
Where we almost, yea, more than married are.
This flea is you and I, and this
Our marriage bed, and marriage temple is.
Though parents grudge, and you, we're met,
And cloister'd in these living walls of jet.
Though use make you apt to kill me,
Let not to that self-murder added be,
And sacrilege, three sins in killing three

Cruel and sudden, hast thou since
Purpled thy nail in blood of innocence?
Wherein could this flea guilty be,
Except in that drop which it suck'd from thee?
Yet thou triumph'st, and say'st that thou
Find'st not thyself nor me the weaker now.
'Tis true; then learn how false fears be;
Just so much honour, when thou yield'st to me,
Will waste, as this flea's death took life from thee.

The Flea, John Donne

Page 223
They therefore went up through the regions of the air, sweetly talking as they went; being comforted, because they safely got over the river, and had such glorious companions to attend them…

The Pilgrim's Progress from This World to That Which Is to Come, John Bunyan

ACKNOWLEDGEMENTS

The History of the Bethel Hospital at Norwich. Built by Mrs Mary Chapman in the year 1713.

Commenced by the late Sir Frederick Bateman and completed by Walter Rye.

Gibbs and Waller, Printers, 31 Colegate Street. Norwich, 1906.

IMAGES

Portrait of Mary (facing page 1 and 228) and photograph of the original section of the Bethel Hospital (page 146)
From Bateman and Rye, 1906.